Welcome to Spanish Series

First Start in Spanish

BLACK-LINE MASTERS

for Practicing Reading and Writing Skills

Myriam Met

Illustrations by Janet E. Lagenaur

National Textbook Company
NTC a division of *NTC Publishing Group* • Lincolnwood, Illinois USA

Published by National Textbook Company, a division of NTC Publishing Group.

Manufactured in the United States of America.

8 9 0 VP 9 8 7 6 5 4 3 2 1

Contents

Introduction

The *First Start in Spanish Black-line Masters* provide opportunities for students to practice reading and writing along with the language skills developed in the *First Start in Spanish Teacher's Manual*. The activities in these masters provide written reinforcement of the vocabulary and concepts in the *Teacher's Manual* and complement the oral/aural reinforcement in the *First Start in Spanish Activities Book*. Like the *Activities Book*, the *First Start in Spanish Black-line Masters* may be used independently of the *Teacher's Manual* to reinforce the vocabulary and concepts developed in many FLES or bilingual courses.

While these worksheets provide written reinforcement of language skills, it is important to note that this is not intended to be a developmental reading and writing program for students of Spanish. Instead, the emphasis is on recognition and reproduction of the written forms of vocabulary.

Because students learning Spanish in elementary school may be at varying grade levels, a range of activities has been provided in this resource book. The activities are generally intended for students in grades two and above. Some activities will be challenging to second graders and easy for older students. Others will be of equal interest and difficulty for students in all grades. Since students' reading and writing abilities vary in the elementary grades and since the activities presented in this resource book have different levels of challenge, teacher judgment with regard to the selection of activities and the amount of assistance provided students will be important in insuring that students derive maximum benefit from the activities. Differing student abilities and types of activities will also influence the amount of time required to complete each page.

It is hoped that teachers and students alike will find the *First Start in Spanish Black-line Masters* a useful and enjoyable means of reinforcing skills in the written forms of Spanish.

Instructions for the Teacher

Lesson 2, Master 1

OBJECTIVE: To practice discrimination between those addressed as *tú* or *Ud.*

DIRECTIONS: Call students' attention to the pictures above each of the boxes. Students should write *tú* in the box if the person or animal would be addressed using *tú*; students write *Ud.* in the boxes below pictures of those appropriately addressed as *Ud.*

Lesson 3, Master 2

OBJECTIVE: To reinforce comprehension of vocabulary from Lessons 1–3; to discriminate between appropriate and inappropriate responses to questions.

DIRECTIONS: Have students circle the sentence which best answers the question.

Lesson 4, Master 3

OBJECTIVE: To reinforce comprehension of *niño, niña,* and *maestra.*

DIRECTIONS: Have students cut out the sentences in the boxes at the bottom of the page and paste them below the pictures they describe.

Lesson 5, Master 4

OBJECTIVE: To reinforce comprehension of vocabulary in Lessons 1–5; to discriminate between appropriate and inappropriate responses to questions.

DIRECTIONS: Have students circle the sentence that best answers the question.

Lesson 6, Master 5

OBJECTIVE: To reinforce comprehension of *me llamo, te llamas, se llama.*

DIRECTIONS: Have students answer each question. For question 3, call students' attention to the pictures at the bottom of the page.

Lesson 7, Master 6

OBJECTIVE: To reinforce comprehension of numbers; to reinforce comprehension of plural forms.

DIRECTIONS: In each box, have students draw a picture which matches the description written beneath it.

Lesson 8, Master 7

OBJECTIVE: To reinforce comprehension of numbers.

DIRECTIONS: Have students circle the number of pictured objects that matches the description given.

Lesson 9, Master 8

OBJECTIVE: To reinforce comprehension of *tener*; to reinforce comprehension of vocabulary and numbers 1–10.

DIRECTIONS: Have students fill in the blanks to correspond with the picture in each box.

Lesson 10, Master 9

OBJECTIVE: To reinforce comprehension of school vocabulary; to reinforce comprehension of numbers 1–10.

DIRECTIONS: Have students furnish the schoolhouse to correspond with the description given.

Lesson 10, Master 10

OBJECTIVE: To reinforce skill in writing classroom vocabulary; to reinforce skill in writing numbers 1–10.

DIRECTIONS: Have students describe Tato's school in the spaces provided. Call to students' attention key vocabulary at the bottom of the page.

Lesson 11, Masters 11–12

OBJECTIVE: To reinforce comprehension of vocabulary in Unit II.

DIRECTIONS: Have students cut out the pictures on Master 11 and paste them in the appropriate boxes on Master 12.

Lesson 12, Master 13

OBJECTIVE: To reinforce comprehension of *para dibujar* and *para cortar.*

DIRECTIONS: Have students cut out the boxed pictures at the bottom of the page and paste them in the appropriate column above.

Lesson 13, Master 14

OBJECTIVE: To reinforce comprehension of *para dibujar, para cortar, para pegar, para escribir.*

DIRECTIONS: For each sentence, have students circle *sí* or *no* as appropriate. At the bottom, students are to draw a picture of something that is not for writing.

Lesson 14, Master 15

OBJECTIVE: To reinforce comprehension of *tener, escribir, dibujar*; to discriminate between appropriate and inappropriate responses to questions.

DIRECTIONS: Have students underline the statement that they would say best answers the teacher's question.

Lesson 15, Master 16

OBJECTIVE: To reinforce comprehension of *tener, pegar*, and *cortar*; to discriminate between appropriate and inappropriate responses to questions.

DIRECTIONS: Have students circle the statement that they would say best answers the teacher's question.

Lesson 16, Master 17

OBJECTIVE: To reinforce skill in writing forms of *cortar, dibujar, escribir*, and *pegar*.

DIRECTIONS: Have students fill in the blanks to complete the answer to each question. For question 5, call students' attention to the picture of Tato at the bottom of the page.

Lesson 17, Master 18

OBJECTIVE: To reinforce comprehension of *presente* and *ausente*; to reinforce skill in writing.

DIRECTIONS: Have students list the names of classmates, indicating whether the person is present or absent, and whether the person is a boy or girl.

Lesson 18, Master 19

OBJECTIVE: To reinforce comprehension of *debajo de, delante de*, and *detrás de*.

DIRECTIONS: In each box have students draw a picture that matches the description written beneath it.

Lesson 19, Master 20

OBJECTIVE: To reinforce comprehension of vocabulary in Unit III.

DIRECTIONS: Call students' attention to the picture of a classroom on Master 20. For each statement below, students circle *sí* if the statement correctly describes the picture; students circle *no* if the statement is incorrect.

Lesson 19, Master 21

OBJECTIVE: To reinforce skill in writing prepositions.

DIRECTIONS: Have students fill in the blanks to correspond with the picture that accompanies each sentence.

Lesson 20, Master 22

OBJECTIVE: To reinforce comprehension of colors.

DIRECTIONS: Have students color each object to match the descriptions given. Students may color the crayon as they wish, then answer the question below the picture.

Lesson 21, Master 23

OBJECTIVE: To reinforce comprehension of colors; to discriminate between masculine and feminine forms.

DIRECTIONS: Have students connect the dots in the sequence you indicate and then describe the complete picture: *el libro.*

Teacher: morado, anaranjado, café, gris, negra, anaranjada, blanco, verde, rojo, amarillo, azul, blanca, roja, amarilla

Lesson 22, Master 24

OBJECTIVE: To reinforce skill in writing; to reinforce comprehension of a poem about the flag.

DIRECTIONS: Have students fill in the blanks in the poem according to the model given. At the bottom of the page, students select one of the flags to color and then describe their flag to the class.

Lesson 23, Master 25

OBJECTIVE: To reinforce comprehension of color vocabulary; to reinforce skill in writing color vocabulary.

DIRECTIONS: Have students complete each sentence as appropriate. Students should color each shape as indicated.

Lesson 24, Master 26

OBJECTIVE: To reinforce comprehension of *tener . . . años.*

DIRECTIONS: Call students' attention to the birthday cakes pictured. Students complete each sentence to correspond to the age indicated on each cake.

Lesson 25, Master 27

OBJECTIVE: To reinforce comprehension of adjectives and adjective agreement.

DIRECTIONS: Have students draw a picture in each box that matches the description written beneath it.

Lesson 25, Master 28

OBJECTIVE: To reinforce comprehension of adjectives and adjective agreement; to reinforce skill in expressing adjectives and adjective agreement.

DIRECTIONS: At the top half of the page, have students match the sentence to the left with the corresponding picture to the right. Students then color each picture. Have students complete the sentences at the bottom of the page according to the colors they used above. Students may be asked to read these sentences to the class.

Lesson 26, Master 29

OBJECTIVE: To reinforce skill in expressing adjectives and adjective agreement; to reinforce comprehension of *flor*.

DIRECTIONS: Have students color each flower as indicated. Students are to complete the sentence in each box to correspond with the flower pictured.

Lesson 26, Master 30

OBJECTIVE: To reinforce skill in expressing adjective agreement using *grande/pequeño*.

DIRECTIONS: Have students write a sentence that describes each picture. Encourage students to use *grande* and *pequeño* in their descriptions.

Lesson 27, Master 31

OBJECTIVE: To reinforce comprehension of the possessive using *de*.

DIRECTIONS: Have students connect the pictures in the first column with those in the second column to correspond with the sentences given below.

Lesson 27, Master 32

OBJECTIVE: To reinforce skill in expressing possession using *de*.

DIRECTIONS: Call students' attention to the pictures of a backpack and of a student desk and chair. Have students answer each question according to the pictures.

Lesson 28, Master 33

OBJECTIVE: To reinforce skill in expressing possession using adjectives.

DIRECTIONS: Have students complete the three exchanges with Tato to correspond with the pictures. Students answer the last three questions as appropriate to them personally.

Lesson 29, Master 34

OBJECTIVE: To reinforce skill in expressing adjective agreement; to reinforce comprehension and expression of possessive adjectives.

DIRECTIONS: Have students color each picture as they wish, and then answer the questions as appropriate.

Lesson 30, Master 35

OBJECTIVE: To reinforce comprehension of vocabulary related to the face.

DIRECTIONS: Have students draw a picture according to the directions given.

Lesson 31, Master 36

OBJECTIVE: To reinforce comprehension of vocabulary related to hair color and facial features.

DIRECTIONS: Have students draw features or color the picture in each box to match the description written beneath it.

Lesson 32, Masters 37–38

OBJECTIVE: To reinforce comprehension of vocabulary related to parts of the body.

DIRECTIONS: Have students cut out the pictures on Master 38 and paste them in the appropriate boxes on Master 37.

Lesson 32, Master 39

OBJECTIVE: To reinforce comprehension of and skill in expressing vocabulary related to parts of the body.

DIRECTIONS: Have students answer each question as appropriate. Accept short answers, such as *Tengo dos.*

Lesson 33, Master 40

OBJECTIVE: To reinforce comprehension of vocabulary related to parts of the body; to reinforce classification skills.

DIRECTIONS: In each row, have students circle the word that does not belong with the others.

Lesson 33, Master 41

OBJECTIVE: To reinforce comprehension of vocabulary related to parts of the body.

DIRECTIONS: Have students connect the dots in the sequence you indicate and then describe the complete picture: *la mano.*

Teacher: la pierna, las orejas, la mano, el cuello, la frente, la nariz, los ojos, los dientes, el pie, el ojo, el dedo, el brazo, la boca, el pelo, la cabeza

Lesson 33, Master 42

OBJECTIVE: To reinforce skill in expressing vocabulary related to parts of the body.

DIRECTIONS: Have students complete the crossword puzzle using the picture clues given at the bottom of the page.

Lesson 34, Master 43

OBJECTIVE: To reinforce comprehension of clothing vocabulary.

DIRECTIONS: Have students draw clothes on the figure in each box to match the description written beneath it. Students then indicate if the statements below are true or false by writing *sí* or *no* as appropriate in the space provided.

Lesson 35, Master 44

OBJECTIVE: To reinforce skill in writing clothing vocabulary and forms of the verb *llevar.*

DIRECTIONS: Have students draw a picture of themselves as they look right now and then provide a written description of what they are wearing.

Lesson 35, Master 45

OBJECTIVE: To reinforce expression of clothing vocabulary; to reinforce classification skills.

DIRECTIONS: Using the vocabulary provided, students indicate whether the clothing is worn by boys, girls, or both by writing the vocabulary in the appropriate box. Point out to students that some words may be used more than once.

Lesson 36, Master 46

OBJECTIVE: To reinforce comprehension of clothing vocabulary.

DIRECTIONS: Have students connect the dots in the sequence you indicate and then describe the completed picture: *los pantalones.*

Teacher: falda, blusa, pantalones, calcetines, camisa, vestido, suéter, zapatos, botas, chaqueta, gorra, mitones.

Lesson 36, Master 47

OBJECTIVE: To reinforce comprehension of the written forms of numerals; to reinforce numerical sequencing.

DIRECTIONS: In each row, have students write the missing number.

Lesson 36, Master 48

OBJECTIVE: To reinforce comprehension of clothing vocabulary.

DIRECTIONS: Have students cut out the vocabulary words at the bottom of the page and paste them beneath the corresponding pictures.

Lesson 37, Master 49

OBJECTIVE: To reinforce comprehension of clothing vocabulary; to reinforce classification skills.

DIRECTIONS: In the space provided have students write *sí* if the statement is true and *no* if it is false.

Lesson 37, Master 50

OBJECTIVE: To reinforce skill in expressing clothing vocabulary.

DIRECTIONS: Have students draw a picture of the teacher and then describe what he or she is wearing in the spaces provided.

Lesson 38, Master 51

OBJECTIVE: To reinforce skill in writing the days of the week; to reinforce calendar skills.

DIRECTIONS: Call students' attention to the calendar provided. Have students complete it as appropriate to the current month. Students use the completed calendar to answer the questions below.

Lesson 39, Master 52

OBJECTIVE: To reinforce recognition of the written forms of numerals and of clothing vocabulary.

DIRECTIONS: Have students find the words listed embedded in the puzzle.

Lesson 39, Master 53

OBJECTIVE: To reinforce skill in writing clothing vocabulary.

DIRECTIONS: Have students complete the crossword puzzle using the picture clues given at the bottom of the page.

Lesson 40, Master 54

OBJECTIVE: To reinforce comprehension of vocabulary related to weather.

DIRECTIONS: In each box, have students draw a picture which matches the description or answers the question written beneath it.

Lesson 41, Master 55

OBJECTIVE: To reinforce recognition of vocabulary related to winter; to reinforce classification skills.

DIRECTIONS: Have students identify those terms at the bottom of the page that are related to winter. These terms are to be cut out and pasted in the grid provided.

Lesson 41, Master 56

OBJECTIVE: To reinforce skill in expressing weather vocabulary.

DIRECTIONS: Have students complete the sentences to correspond with the picture provided OR use the paragraph as a modified dictation:

Teacher: Es un día de invierno. Hace frío. El niño se llama Tony. Tony lleva una chaqueta, una gorra y botas. Tony no tiene frío.

Students then answer the questions at the bottom of the page.

Lesson 41, Master 57

OBJECTIVE: To reinforce skill in writing weather and clothing vocabulary.

DIRECTIONS: Have students complete the paragraph by selecting appropriate vocabulary from the words provided. Point out to students that there may be more than one appropriate choice for several of the blanks. At the bottom of the page, have the students draw a picture of winter.

Lesson 42, Master 58

OBJECTIVE: To reinforce comprehension of *querer*; to reinforce skill in writing toy vocabulary.

DIRECTIONS: Have students connect the children in the first column with any of the toys in the second column. Students then answer the questions below accordingly.

Lesson 43, Master 59

OBJECTIVE: To reinforce skill in describing weather.

DIRECTIONS: Next to each box, have students write a description of the weather pictured.

Lesson 44, Master 60

OBJECTIVE: To reinforce comprehension of toy vocabulary.

DIRECTIONS: Have students color or draw a picture in each box, following the directions given at the bottom of the page.

Lesson 44, Master 61

OBJECTIVE: To reinforce skill in writing toy vocabulary; to reinforce comprehension of *querer*.

DIRECTIONS: Have students list in the first column the names of toys they have; in the second column, students list toys they would like to have.

Lesson 44, Master 62

OBJECTIVE: To reinforce skill in writing toy vocabulary.

DIRECTIONS: Have students complete the crossword, using the picture clues given at the bottom of the page.

Lesson 45, Master 63

OBJECTIVE: To reinforce comprehension of vocabulary related to school workers.

DIRECTIONS: Have students write the names of the persons in your school as indicated.

Lesson 46, Master 64

OBJECTIVE: To reinforce comprehension of the verb *ir*.

DIRECTIONS: In each circle, have students write the number that corresponds to Luis' description of where he is going.

Lesson 46, Master 65

OBJECTIVE: To reinforce skill in writing forms of the verb *ir*.

DIRECTIONS: Have students write numbers in the picture given to indicate where they are going in the classroom and the order in which they will go there. At the bottom of the page, students provide a written description according to the order indicated in the picture.

Lesson 47, Master 66

OBJECTIVE: To reinforce comprehension of *¡vayan!*

DIRECTIONS: Have students select any five commands from those at the bottom of the page. These are cut out and pasted in any order at the top. Each student selects two classmates who must read and carry out the directions given.

Lesson 47, Master 67

OBJECTIVE: To reinforce skill in expressing *va con*.

DIRECTIONS: Each of the items listed at the top of the page goes with a word at the bottom. Students complete each sentence by choosing a word from the list at the bottom of the page. Example: *El papel va con el lápiz.*

Lesson 48, Master 68

OBJECTIVE: To reinforce skill in expressing actions.

DIRECTIONS: Call students' attention to the pictures provided. Have students write a sentence to describe the action pictured.

Lesson 49, Master 69

OBJECTIVE: To reinforce comprehension of vocabulary related to the playground; to reinforce reading skills.

DIRECTIONS: Have students read the paragraph and then answer the questions below.

Lesson 49, Master 70

OBJECTIVE: To reinforce comprehension of *primero, segundo, tercero.*

DIRECTIONS: Have students cut out the pictures of children and place them in line according to the description provided.

Lesson 49, Master 71

OBJECTIVE: To reinforce skill in expressing vocabulary related to the playground.

DIRECTIONS: Call students' attention to the picture provided. Students use this picture to answer the questions below.

Lesson 50, Master 72

OBJECTIVE: To reinforce comprehension of vocabulary related to the school and school workers; to reinforce word order skills.

DIRECTIONS: Have students rewrite the scrambled sentences so that they make sense. You may want to point out to students that each sentence has two clues in it: an uppercase letter begins the first word of the sentence and a period comes after the final word in the sentence.

Lesson 51, Master 73

OBJECTIVE: To reinforce comprehension and expression of the constructions *me, te, le falta*.

DIRECTIONS: Have students read the conversation between the teacher, the students, and Tato, and complete the conversation by filling in the blanks.

Lesson 52, Master 74

OBJECTIVE: To reinforce comprehension of the months of the year.

DIRECTIONS: Survey the class to find out in which months students have their birthdays. As you call on individuals in turn, students fill in the names of classmates after the appropriate month. In a large class, students may need an extra sheet of paper to fill in all their classmates' names.

Lesson 52, Master 75

OBJECTIVE: To reinforce skill in writing the months of the year.

DIRECTIONS: Have students fill in the blanks according to the model provided. Students then answer the questions below.

Lesson 52, Master 76

OBJECTIVE: To reinforce skill in expressing the future using *ir a*.

DIRECTIONS: Have students refer to the pictures of Tato and then write a sentence to describe what Tato is going to do.

Lesson 53, Master 77

OBJECTIVE: To reinforce comprehension of *hablar*.

DIRECTIONS: Have students circle *sí* if the statement is true and *no* if it is false.

Lesson 53, Master 78

OBJECTIVE: To reinforce skill in writing vocabulary and constructions taught in Unit IX.

DIRECTIONS: Have students write the answer to each question. At the bottom of the page, students may draw a picture that illustrates the answer to question 4 or 5.

Lesson 54, Master 79

OBJECTIVE: To reinforce comprehension of vocabulary and constructions taught in Unit IX.

DIRECTIONS: Have students read the conversation between Susana and Miguel. Students draw a picture to illustrate the conclusion of the conversation.

Lesson 54, Master 80

OBJECTIVE: To reinforce skill in writing vocabulary and constructions taught in Unit IX.

DIRECTIONS: Have students read the conversation between Pepe and Juana, filling in the blanks as appropriate.

Lesson 55, Master 81

OBJECTIVE: To reinforce skill in expressing vocabulary related to the family.

DIRECTIONS: Call students' attention to the picture at the bottom of the page. Students complete each sentence according to the picture.

Lesson 56, Master 82

OBJECTIVE: To reinforce skill in writing about personal and family information.

DIRECTIONS: Have students complete the sentences as appropriate to them. At the bottom, students draw a picture of their grandparents.

Lesson 57, Master 83

OBJECTIVE: To reinforce comprehension of family vocabulary.

DIRECTIONS: Have students draw a line from each word to the corresponding picture.

Lesson 57, Master 84

OBJECTIVE: To reinforce comprehension of family vocabulary.

DIRECTIONS: Call students' attention to the four pictures of families. Students refer to these pictures to indicate in which apartment each family lives.

Lesson 57, Master 85

OBJECTIVE: To reinforce skill in writing about personal and family information.

DIRECTIONS: Have students answer the questions in the spaces provided.

Lesson 57, Master 86

OBJECTIVE: To reinforce skill in writing about personal and family information.

DIRECTIONS: Have students complete each sentence about their own families and activities in their homes.

Lesson 58, Master 87

OBJECTIVE: To reinforce comprehension of *tío(s)* and *primo(-a)(s)*.

DIRECTIONS: Have students draw pictures of an aunt, uncle, or aunt and uncle in the box provided. Students write the names of the persons pictured below the box. If these persons have children, pictures of the students' cousins are to be drawn in the second box, and the names of the cousins written below the picture. Students then answer the questions at the bottom of the page.

Lesson 59, Master 88

OBJECTIVE: To reinforce comprehension of family vocabulary.

DIRECTIONS: For each of the questions given, survey the class to find out to how many of the students each question applies. Students write the number in the column to the right. As a follow-up you may want to have students summarize the results orally when the survey is complete.

OR: Students may be given five minutes to find as many people as they can in the class who answer *sí* in response to the descriptors provided. At the end of the time period, call on students to find out how many people they found for each category.

Lesson 59, Master 89

OBJECTIVE: To reinforce skill in writing personal and family information.

DIRECTIONS: Have each student interview a partner to complete the form provided. Students may be asked to report this information back to the class.

Lesson 60, Master 90

OBJECTIVE: To reinforce comprehension of animal vocabulary; to reinforce classification skills.

DIRECTIONS: Have students cut out the words at the bottom of the page and paste them in the appropriate columns to indicate whether the person or animal lives in a house or barn. Note: students may put *un perro* and *un gato* in either column.

Lesson 61, Master 91

OBJECTIVE: To reinforce comprehension of vocabulary related to animals and animal bodies.

DIRECTIONS: Have students draw a picture in each box to match the description written beneath it.

Lesson 61, Master 92

OBJECTIVE: To reinforce skill in writing vocabulary related to animals.

DIRECTIONS: Have students complete the crossword, using the picture clues given at the bottom of the page.

Lesson 62, Master 93

OBJECTIVE: To reinforce comprehension of animal vocabulary; to reinforce skills in classifying animal families.

DIRECTIONS: Have students cut out the vocabulary words at the bottom of the page and paste them in the appropriate columns to indicate animal families. Students then complete the statements at the bottom of the page.

Lesson 63, Masters 94–95

OBJECTIVE: To reinforce skill in writing vocabulary related to animals.

DIRECTIONS: Have students draw a picture of an imaginary animal on Master 94 and then use their picture to answer the questions on Master 95.

Lesson 64, Master 96

OBJECTIVE: To reinforce comprehension of vocabulary in Units I–XI.

DIRECTIONS: In each row, have students select the word from the column on the right that best completes the series.

Lesson 64, Master 97

OBJECTIVE: To reinforce skill in expressing and describing vocabulary from Units I–XI.

DIRECTIONS: Have students color each picture as they wish and then write a description of the picture in the space provided below each box.

Lesson 65, Master 98

OBJECTIVE: To reinforce comprehension of vocabulary from Units I–XI; to reinforce skills in comparing and contrasting.

DIRECTIONS: Have students read each sentence. Students write *sí* or *no* in the first column to indicate whether the statement applies to people; similarly, students write *sí* or *no* in the second column to indicate whether the statement applies to animals.

Lesson 65, Master 99

OBJECTIVE: To reinforce skill in expressing the functions of objects.

DIRECTIONS: Have students answer each question with a verb that indicates the function of the object named.

Lesson 65, Master 100

OBJECTIVE: To reinforce skill in writing vocabulary from Lessons 1–63.

DIRECTIONS: Have students complete the crossword using the picture clues given at the bottom of the page.

Answer Key

Master 1

tú tú Ud.
Ud. tú tú

Master 2

1. c
2. a
3. b
4. a
5. c

Master 3

Es niña. Es maestro. Es niño.
Son niñas. Es maestra. Son niños.

Master 4

1. a
2. b
3. a
4. b
5. b

Master 5

3. Marisol

Master 8

ocho dos
seis
siete una

Master 10

dos clases, tres maestras, nueve niños, dos puertas y seis ventanas

Master 13

Para dibujar	*Para cortar*
crayon	axe
chalk	jackknife
marker	scissors
pencil	knife
pen	saw

Master 14

1. No
2. Sí
3. No
4. No
5. Sí
6. No
7. No
8. Sí
9. No
10. No

Master 15

1. b
2. c
3. a
4. a
5. c

Master 16

1. b
2. c
3. a
4. a
5. c

Master 17

1. Escribo
2. Dibujo
3. Corto
4. Pego
5. Corta, pega, dibuja y escribe.

Master 20

Sí
No
Sí
Sí
Sí
No

Master 21

1. debajo
2. detrás
3. detrás
4. delante
5. debajo
6. delante

Master 25

morado
verde
anaranjado
gris
pardo

Master 26

cuatro
diez
cinco
dos
seis
ocho
tres
siete

Master 29

rojas
grandes y amarillas
pequeñas
pequeña y blanca

Master 30

Son dos creyones grandes.
Son tres tijeras pequeñas.
Son cuatro papeles pequeños.
Es un libro grande.
Son dos sillas grandes.

Master 32

1. Los libros son de Miguel.
2. La silla es de Eva.
3. Los lápices son de Miguel.
4. Las tijeras son de Miguel.
5. La pasta es de Eva.

Master 33

1. mi
2. su
3. tu

Master 39

1. Tengo dos brazos.
2. Tengo dos ojos.
3. Tengo cinco dedos en una mano.
4. Tengo dos manos.
5. Tengo diez dedos en dos manos.
6. Tengo dos orejas.

Master 40

1. bandera
2. pasta
3. maestra
4. tijeras
5. verde
6. azul
7. papeles
8. manos
9. pierna
10. ojos rojos

Master 42

Horizontal

2. cara
3. mano
4. dedo
6. pie
7. cuello
10. orejas
11. boca
12. nariz

Vertical

1. frente
5. dientes
6. pierna
8. ojos
9. pelo
11. brazo

Master 43

1. No
2. No
3. No
4. No
5. Sí

Master 47

catorce
trece
dieciocho
dieciséis
diecisiete
quince
diecinueve

Master 49

1. Sí
2. No
3. Sí
4. Sí
5. No
6. No *or* Sí
7. Sí
8. No
9. Sí
10. No *or* Sí

Master 52

```
J K T R E I N T A B X M M B H
M E D I E C I S I E T E V L K
L X O A N X R V Z E Q L W U N
C F E O G W Z A P A T O S S D
Z A V U U D O C E X C E E A O
L X L A W X D I U D A F N B G
Y Q T C T R E C E B T J J J Q
G F B R E B X A E N O X H R V
A A S H R T V Q L I R Q J T V
M L N M U L I O O V C T Y I R
O D Q E C J E N N O E G S O R
M A G C Z C F V E C I Y K V X
I N L X I I X H L S E X I T Q
S F W M R A F V E I N T E Q F
Q R G Q U I N C E H N T X Y B
```

Master 53

Horizontal	*Vertical*
1. botas	1. blusa
3. falda	2. pantalones
5. zapatos	4. chaqueta
7. camisa	6. guantes
8. vestido	

Master 56

invierno, enero, febrero, etc.
frío
gorra, mitones, botas, etc.
gorra, mitones, botas, etc.
calor

Master 59

Sample sentences:
Hace sol. Hace frío. Es el invierno.
Llueve. Hace viento. Es el otoño.
Hace sol. Hace calor. Es el verano.

Master 62

Horizontal	*Vertical*
2. bicicleta	1. globo
3. coche	3. camión
4. muñeca	6. avión
5. cometa	7. pito
7. patines	
8. pelota	

Master 67

El papel va con el lápiz.
El pelo va con la cabeza.
El brazo va con la mano.
La falda va con la blusa.
La secretaria va con la oficina
La silla va con el pupitre.
La cometa va con el viento.
Los calcetines van con los zapatos.
Los dientes van con la boca.
Los pantalones van con la camisa.

Master 68

La niña corre.
La niña brinca la cuerda.
Los niños corren.

Master 71

1. Los niños están en el patio de recreo.
2a. Una niña juega a la rayuela.
2b. Una niña brinca la cuerda.
2c. El niño juega con la pelota.

Master 72

1. La principal trabaja en la oficina.
2. Hay muchos libros en la biblioteca.
3. Los niños van al patio de recreo para jugar.
4. El patio de recreo está afuera.
5. No corro en la clase.
6. Los niños brincan la cuerda.

Master 73

1. tiza
2. falta un lápiz
3. Te

Master 75

Treinta días tiene septiembre,
abril, junio y noviembre;
febrero tiene veintiocho,
y los demás treinta y uno.
treinta
treinta
treinta
treinta
veintiocho

Master 76

1. Tato va a escribir.
2. Tato va a brincar la cuerda.
3. Tato va a cortar.
4. Tato va a jugar con la cometa.
5. Tato va a pegar.
6. Tato va a llevar la chaqueta.

Master 77

1. Sí
2. No
3. No
4. No
5. Sí *or* No
6. No
7. Sí *or* No
8. Sí
9. No
10. Sí
11. No
12. Sí *or* No

Master 80

teléfono
español

Habla
Pepe
Bien
jugar
pequeño
cometa

Master 81

1. La mamá
2. El papá
3. La hermana
4. El hermano
5. El hermano
6. mamá, papá, hermana, hermanos

Master 84

1. 6
2. 3
3. 2
4. 10

Master 90

House	*Barn*
un señor	un perro
un perro	un gato
un gato	un gallo
una abuela	una vaca
un bebé	un pollito
una niña	un caballo
mi primo	una gallina

Master 92

Horizontal	*Vertical*
2. oveja	1. conejo
5. establo	3. granja
6. vaca	4. cola
8. pato	7. patito
9. ala	
10. gallina	

Master 93

1. gallo
2. vaca
3. patito

Master 96

1. cinco
2. pollito
3. cometa
4. abrigo
5. nieva
6. domingo
7. boca
8. la bibliotecaria
9. verde
10. trece

Master 98

1. no sí
2. sí no
3. sí sí
4. no sí
5. sí sí *or* no
6. sí sí
7. sí no
8. no sí
9. no no
10. sí sí

Master 99

1. hablar
2. escribir
3. jugar
4. correr
5. llevar
6. hablar
7. pegar
8. brincar
9. dibujar
10. cortar

Master 100

Horizontal	*Vertical*
2. abuelo	1. zapatos
4. pupitre	3. blusa
8. caballo	5. pito
9. libro	6. falda
10. enfermera	7. doce
12. patines	11. mano

Nombre ________________________________

¿Tú o usted?

Nombre ______________________________

Escoge

1. Buenos días. ¿Cómo estás tú?

   a. Soy Tato. b. Es un niño.

   c. Muy bien, gracias.

2. ¿Quién eres tú?

   a. Soy Tato. b. ¡Hola!

   c. Es un niño.

3. ¿Qué es?

   a. Muy bien, gracias. b. Es un niño.

   c. Soy Tato.

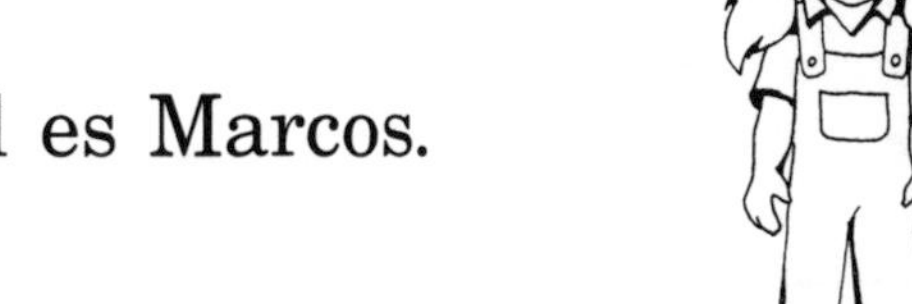

4. ¿Quién es ella?

   a. Ella es Susana. b. Él es Marcos.

   c. Soy Tato.

5. ¿Eres un niño?

   a. Sí, soy Susana. b. ¿Quién eres tú?

   c. Sí, soy un niño.

Nombre ____________________

¿Quién es?

____________________ ____________________ ____________________

____________________ ____________________ ____________________

Son niñas.	Es niño.	Son niños.
Es maestro.	Es niña.	Es maestra.

Nombre ______________________________

María

1. ¿Quién es ella?

   a. Ella es María. b. Él es Mario.

   c. Es la maestra.

2. ¿Es María niño?

   a. Sí, es niño. b. No. María es niña.

   c. Soy Tato.

3. ¿Es María maestra?

   a. No. No es maestra. b. No. No es María.

   c. Sí, es maestra.

4. ¿Qué es María?

   a. María es niño. b. María es niña.

   c. María es maestra.

5. ¿Cómo está María?

   a. Está muy bien. b. Está muy mal.

   c. Está así así.

Nombre ______________________________

Contesta

1. ¿Cómo te llamas?

____

2. ¿Cómo se llama la maestra?

____

3. ¿Cómo se llama la niña?

____

David

Marisol

Arturo

Gabriel

Nombre ______________________

Dibuja

Son cinco lápices.

Son tres niñas.

Son cuatro papeles.

Son dos creyones.

Es un lápiz.

Nombre ______________________

¿Cuántos son?

Circula

Son ocho pupitres.

Son seis libros.

Son nueve sillas.

Son siete creyones.

Son diez lápices.

Nombre ______________________________

Completa

La maestra: Tato, ¿cuántos lápices tienes?

Tato: Tengo _____ lápices.

La maestra: Tato, ¿cuántos libros tienes?

Tato: Tengo ______ libros.

La maestra: Tato, ¿cuántos creyones tienes?

Tato: Tengo ___ creyones.

La maestra: Tato, ¿cuántos papeles tienes?

Tato: Tengo _____ papeles.

La maestra: Tato, ¿Cuántas sillas tienes?

Tato: Tengo _______ silla.

Nombre ______________________________

Dibuja

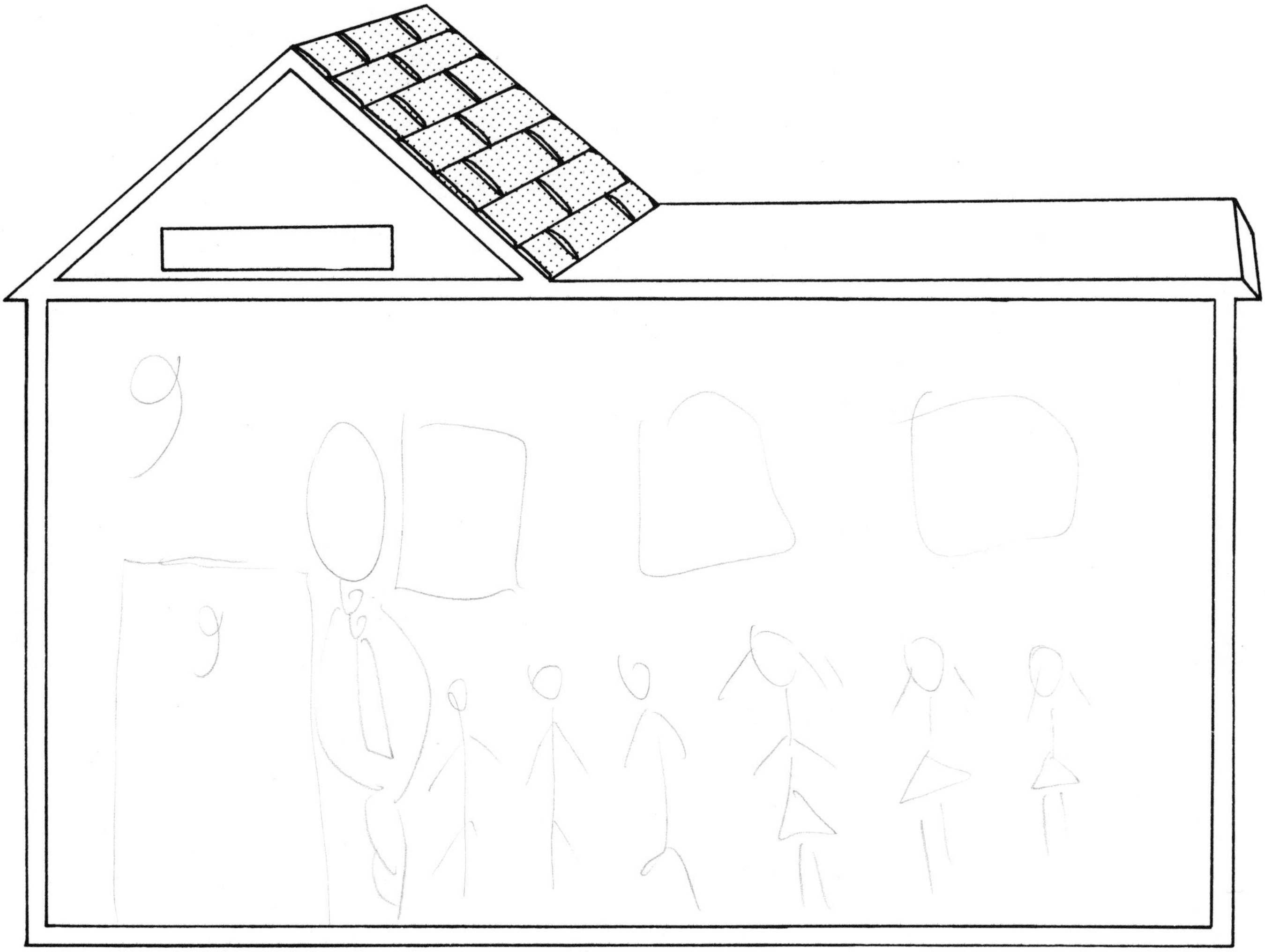

La escuela tiene una puerta.
La escuela tiene tres ventanas.
La escuela tiene tres niños y tres niñas.
La clase tiene un maestro.
El número de la clase es nueve.

Nombre ______________________

La escuela de Tato

La escuela de Tato tiene:

____

____

____

____

____

____

____

____

ventanas puertas clases maestras niños

Nombre ______________________________

La escuela

el creyón	la tiza	el pupitre
la escuela	la silla	la pizarra
el libro	las tijeras	la puerta
la pasta	los papeles	la ventana

La escuela

(página 2)

2+3=5

Nombre ______________________________

¿Para qué es?

Para dibujar	Para cortar

Nombre ______________________________

¿Sí o no?

1.	Las tijeras son para dibujar.	Sí	No
2.	La pasta es para pegar.	Sí	No
3.	El papel es para escribir.	Sí	No
4.	La puerta es para pegar.	Sí	No
5.	El creyón es para dibujar.	Sí	No
6.	El lápiz es para cortar.	Sí	No
7.	La silla es para dibujar.	Sí	No
8.	Las tijeras son para cortar.	Sí	No
9.	La ventana es para escribir.	Sí	No
10.	El pupitre es para cortar.	Sí	No

Dibuja
No es para escribir

Nombre ______________________

Yo contesto

1. **La maestra:** ¿Tienes un lápiz?

   Yo: a. Sí. Tienes un lápiz.

   b. Sí. Escribo con el lápiz.

   c. Sí. Dibujo con la maestra.

2. **La maestra:** ¿Tienes un creyón?

   Yo: a. Sí. Tengo un lápiz.

   b. Sí. Escribo con el lápiz.

   c. Sí. Dibujo con el creyón.

3. **La maestra:** ¿Qué haces con el lápiz?

   Yo: a. Escribo con el lápiz.

   b. Tato escribe con el lápiz.

   c. Tú escribes con el lápiz.

4. **La maestra:** ¿Qué haces con el creyón?

   Yo: a. Dibujo con el creyón.

   b. Tato dibuja con el creyón.

   c. Tú dibujas con el creyón.

5. **La maestra:** ¿Tiene Tato un lápiz y un papel?

   Yo: a. Sí. Yo escribo con el lápiz y el papel.

   b. Sí. Tú escribes con el lápiz y el papel.

   c. Sí. Él escribe con el lápiz y el papel.

Nombre ______________________________

Yo contesto

1. **La maestra:** ¿Tienes la pasta?

   Yo: a. Sí. Tienes la pasta.

   b. Sí. Pego con la pasta.

   c. Sí. Corto con Tato.

2. **La maestra:** ¿Tienes las tijeras?

   Yo: a. Sí. Tengo la pasta.

   b. Sí. Pego con la pasta.

   c. Sí. Corto con las tijeras.

3. **La maestra:** ¿Qué haces con la pasta?

   Yo: a. Pego con la pasta.

   b. Tú pegas con la pasta.

   c. Tato pega con la pasta.

4. **La maestra:** ¿Qué haces con las tijeras?

   Yo: a. Corto con las tijeras.

   b. Tato corta con las tijeras.

   c. Cortas con las tijeras.

5. **La maestra:** ¿Tiene Tato las tijeras y la pasta?

   Yo: a. Sí. Yo corto y yo pego.

   b. Sí. Tú cortas y tú pegas.

   c. Sí. Él corta y él pega.

Nombre ______________________________

Contesta

1. ¿Qué haces con el lápiz?

   ______________________________ con el lápiz.

2. ¿Qué haces con el creyón?

   ______________________________ con el creyón.

3. ¿Qué haces con las tijeras?

   ______________________________ con las tijeras.

4. ¿Qué haces con la pasta?

   ______________________________ con la pasta.

5. ¿Qué hace Tato?

   ____

   ____

   ____

   ____

   ____

   ____

Nombre ______________________

Nuestra clase

Nombre	¿Presente o ausente?	¿Niño o niña?
1. ____	____	____
2. ____	____	____
3. ____	____	____
4. ____	____	____
5. ____	____	____
6. ____	____	____
7. ____	____	____
8. ____	____	____
9. ____	____	____
10. ____	____	____

Nombre ______________________________

Dibuja

Un libro debajo de una silla.

Una niña delante de un pupitre.

Un niño detrás de una puerta.

Un papel debajo de un libro.

Una niña detrás de un niño.

Nombre ____________________

La clase de español

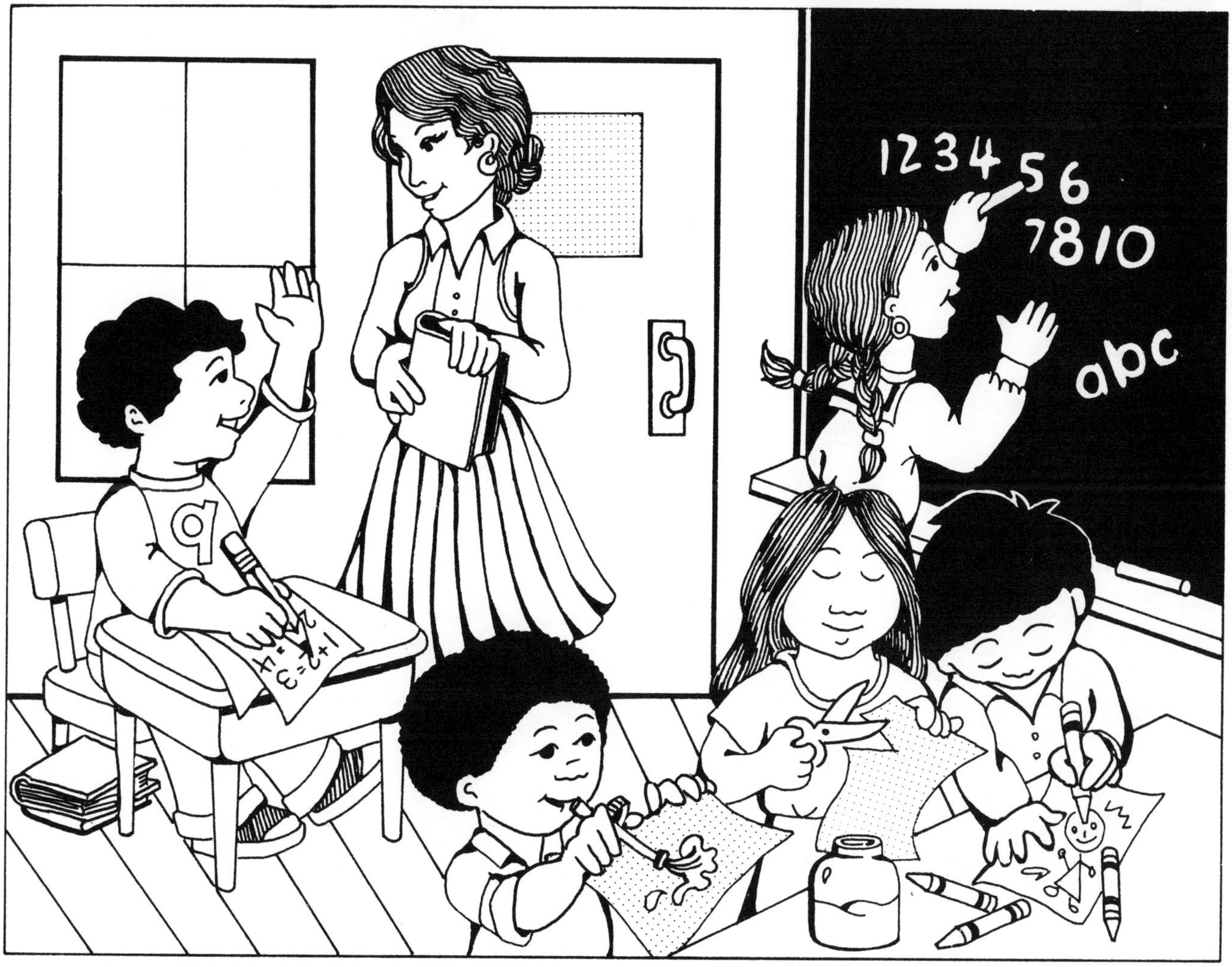

La maestra está delante de la puerta. Sí No

Dos niñas dibujan. Sí No

Una niña corta con tijeras. Sí No

Un niño escribe con el lápiz. Sí No

Hay una puerta y una ventana. Sí No

Hay dos libros detrás de la pizarra. Sí No

Nombre ______________________________

Completa

1. La pasta está ______________________

   de las tijeras.

2. La maestra está ______________________

   del pupitre.

3. La niña está ______________________

   de la puerta.

4. El niño está ______________________

   de la maestra.

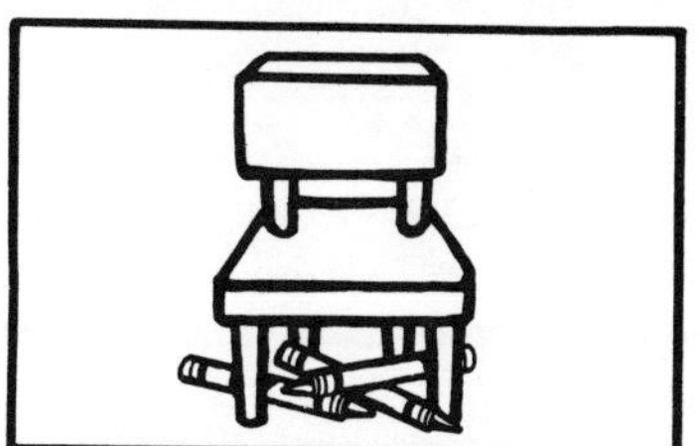

5. Los creyones están ______________________

   de la silla.

6. Los niños están ______________________

   de la ventana.

Nombre ______________________________

Colorea

La tiza es blanca.

El lápiz es verde.

La puerta es roja.

El libro es azul.

El papel es amarillo.

Colorea y contesta:

¿De qué color es el creyón?

____

Nombre ______________________________

¿Qué es?

café

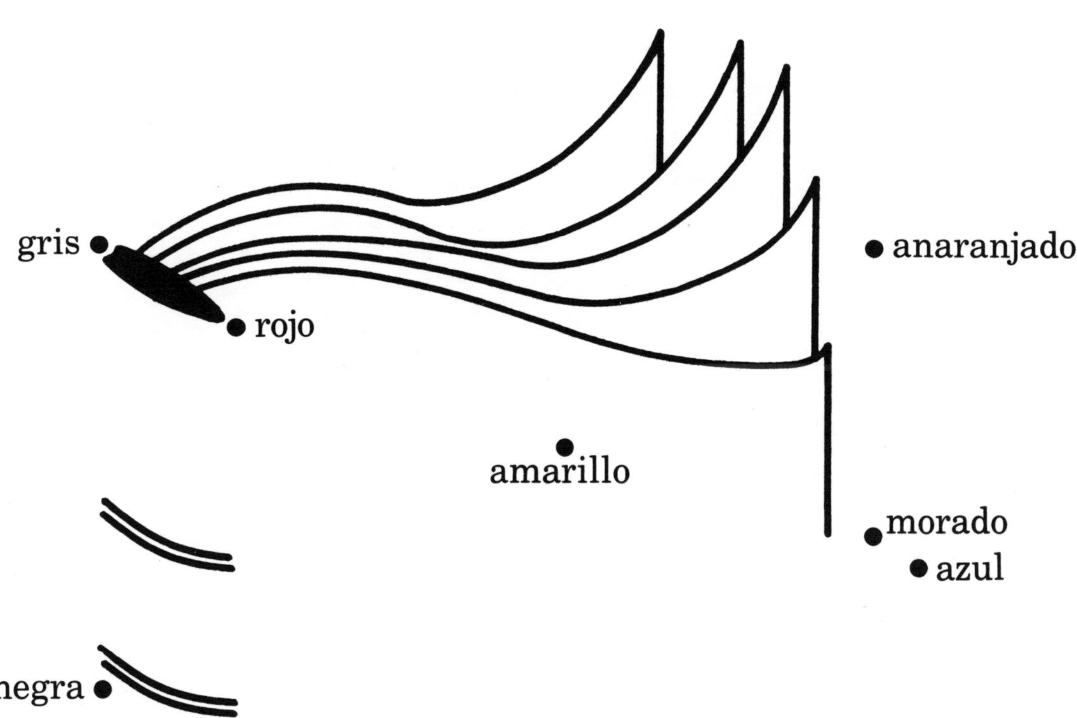

verde

blanca

anaranjada

blanco

amarilla

roja

Nombre ______________________________

La bandera

Roja, blanca y azul.
¡Qué bonita es mi bandera!
Yo te amo y respeto
Símbolo de mi tierra.

______________, blanca y azul.

¡Qué ______________ es mi ______________!

______________ te amo y respeto,

Símbolo de mi ______________.

Colorea

Mi bandera

Nombre ______________________________

Colorea y escribe

rojo y azul hacen ______________________________

amarillo y azul hacen ______________________________

amarillo y rojo hacen ______________________________

negro y blanco hacen ______________________________

morado y amarillo hacen ______________________________

Nombre ____________________

¡Feliz cumpleaños!

¡Feliz cumpleaños, Pablo!

¡Feliz cumpleaños, Ana!

¡Feliz cumpleaños, Clara!

¡Feliz cumpleaños, Paquita!

¡Feliz cumpleaños, Beto!

¡Feliz cumpleaños, Tomás!

¡Feliz cumpleaños, Lourdes!

¡Feliz cumpleaños, Manuel!

Pablo tiene ____________________ años.

Ana tiene ____________________ años.

Clara tiene ____________________ años.

Paquita tiene ____________________ años.

Beto tiene ____________________ años.

Tomás tiene ____________________ años.

Lourdes tiene ____________________ años.

Manuel tiene ____________________ años.

Nombre ______________________________

Dibuja y colorea

Un libro grande y un libro pequeño.

Cinco lápices pequeños.

Cuatro creyones rojos.

Dos puertas verdes.

Dos niños pequeños.

Nombre ______________________________

Aparea y colorea

Un lápiz pequeño.

Dos lápices grandes.

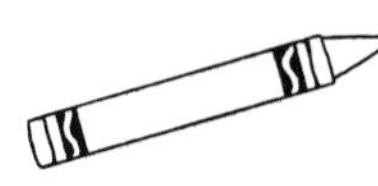

Dos libros grandes.

Dos libros pequeños.

Un creyón pequeño.

¿De qué color son?

1. El lápiz pequeño es ______________________________.
2. Los lápices grandes son ______________________________.
3. Los libros grandes son ______________________________.
4. Los libros pequeños son ______________________________.
5. El creyón pequeño es ______________________________.

Nombre ____________________

Los Colores

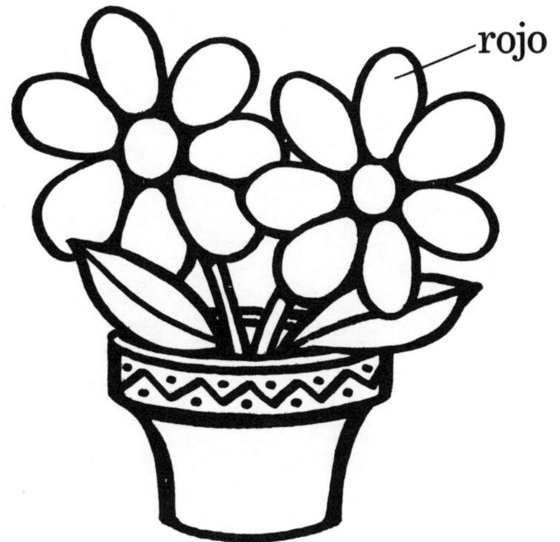

Las flores son

________________.

Las flores no son grandes.

Son ________________.

Las flores son ________________

y ________________.

Una flor ________________

y ________________.

Nombre ______________________________

Escribe

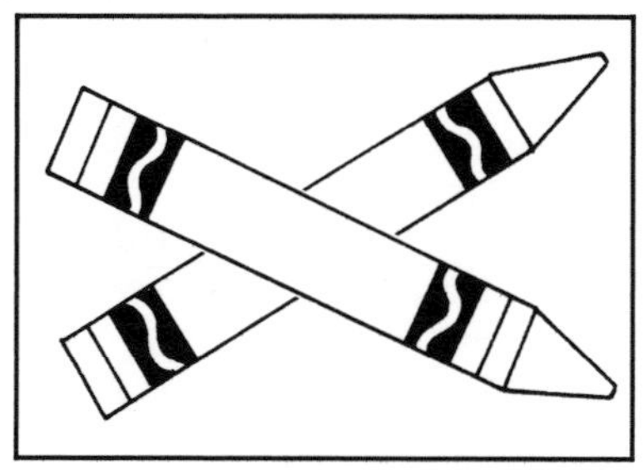

Son ______________________________

____

____

____

____

____

Es ______________________________

____

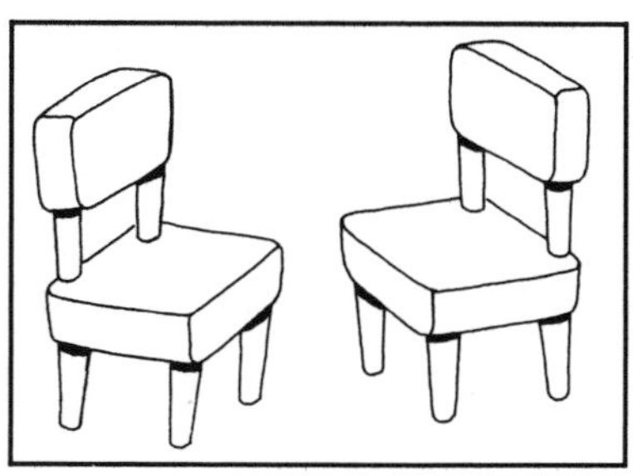

____

____

Nombre ____________________

Aparea

Los creyones son de Rosa.

Los lápices son de Alberto.

El libro es de Ana.

Los papeles son de Mateo.

Los libros grandes son de Rosa.

Las tijeras son de Alberto.

La pasta es de Ana.

Nombre ______________________

¿De quién son?

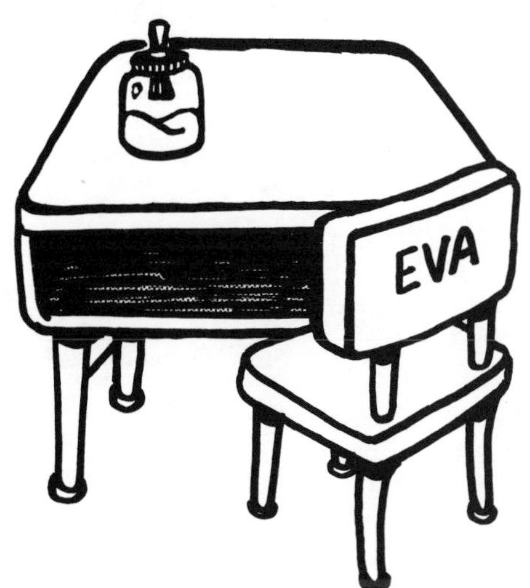

1. ¿De quién son los libros?

____

2. ¿De quién es la silla?

____

3. ¿De quién son los lápices?

____

4. ¿De quién son las tijeras?

____

5. ¿De quién es la pasta?

____

Nombre ______________________________

Tato contesta

1. **La maestra:** Tato, ¿es tu papel?

   Tato: No. No es ____________ papel.

2. **La maestra:** Tato, ¿es el papel de Jaime?

   Tato: Sí. Es ____________ papel.

3. **La maestra:** Tato, ¿es ____________ lápiz?

   Tato: Sí. Es mi lápiz.

Yo contesto

1. ¿De qué color es tu pasta?

____

2. ¿Es tu silla grande o pequeña?

____

3. ¿Estás delante de tu pupitre?

____

____

Nombre ______________________

Colorea y contesta

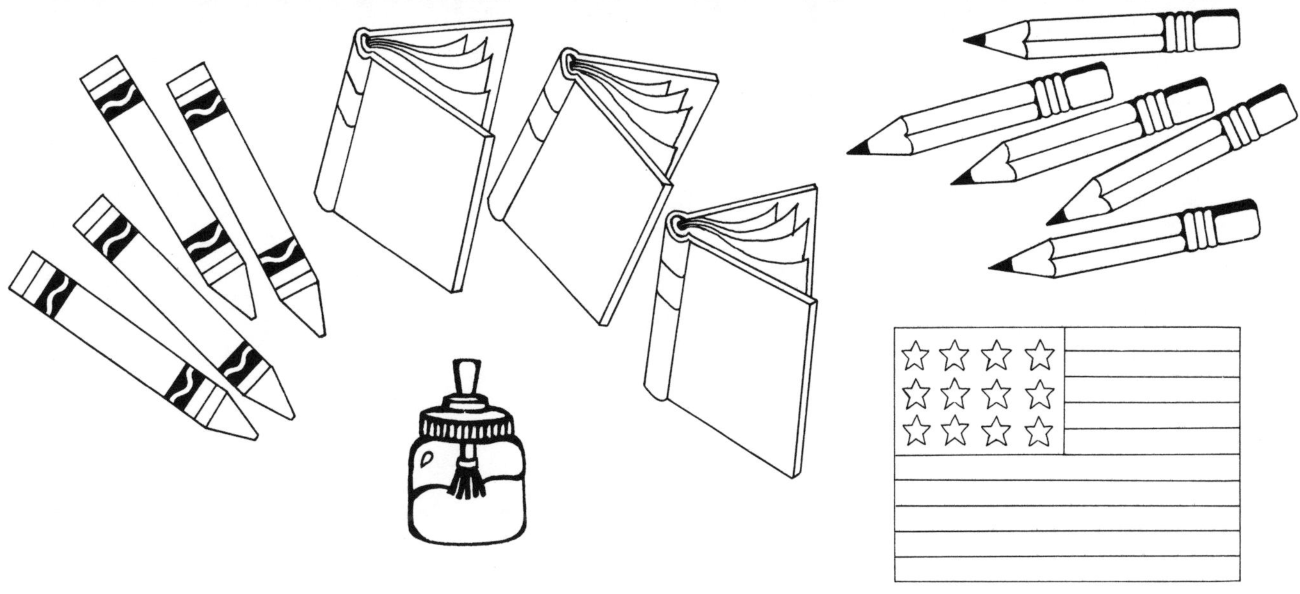

1. ¿De qué color es tu bandera?

____

2. ¿De qué color son tus creyones?

____

3. ¿De qué color son tus lápices?

____

4. ¿De qué color es tu pasta?

____

5. ¿De qué color son tus libros?

____

Nombre ______________________________

Dibuja y colorea

1. Dibuja una cabeza.

2. Dibuja pelo negro en la cabeza.

3. Dibuja unos ojos azules en la cabeza.

4. Dibuja una nariz grande en la cabeza.

5. Dibuja una boca pequeña en la cabeza.

6. Dibuja dos orejas grandes en la cabeza.

Nombre ___________________________________

Dibuja o colorea

Tiene el pelo castaño.

Es rubio.

Tiene dientes grandes.

Es moreno.

Dibuja un cuello.

Nombre ______________________________

Las partes del cuerpo

la pierna	las orejas	la frente
los ojos	el pie	la boca
el brazo	el dedo	los dientes
la nariz	el cuello	la mano

Las partes del cuerpo

(página 2)

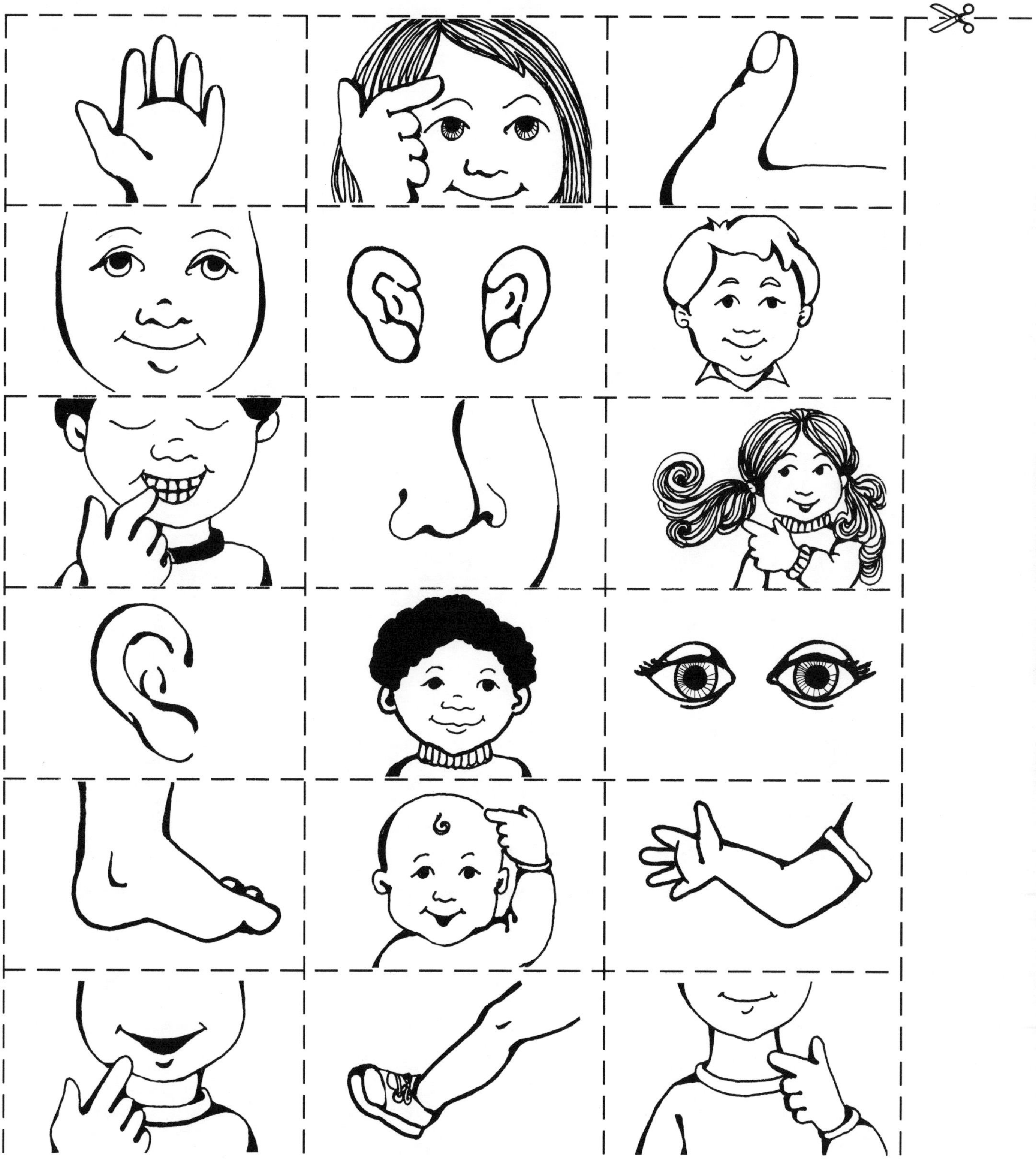

Nombre ______________________________

¿Cuántos tienes?

1. ¿Cuántos brazos tienes?

____

2. ¿Cuántos ojos tienes?

____

3. ¿Cuántos dedos tienes en una mano?

____

4. ¿Cuántas manos tienes?

____

5. ¿Cuántos dedos tienes en dos manos?

____

6. ¿Cuántas orejas tienes?

____

Nombre ______________________________

¡No está bien!

1. mano frente bandera cabeza
2. dedo pasta ojo pelo
3. cuello pie mano maestra
4. tijeras boca pierna oreja
5. moreno rubio castaño verde
6. dientes ojos orejas azul
7. cabeza piernas brazos papeles
8. cuello cabeza manos cara
9. dientes boca frente pierna
10. ojos negros ojos rojos ojos azules ojos pardos

Nombre ______________________________

¿Qué es?

los dientes

los ojos

la frente

el ojo

el cuello

el dedo

el pelo

la boca

las orejas

el pie

la nariz

el brazo

la mano

la cabeza

la pierna

Nombre ______________________________

Crucigrama

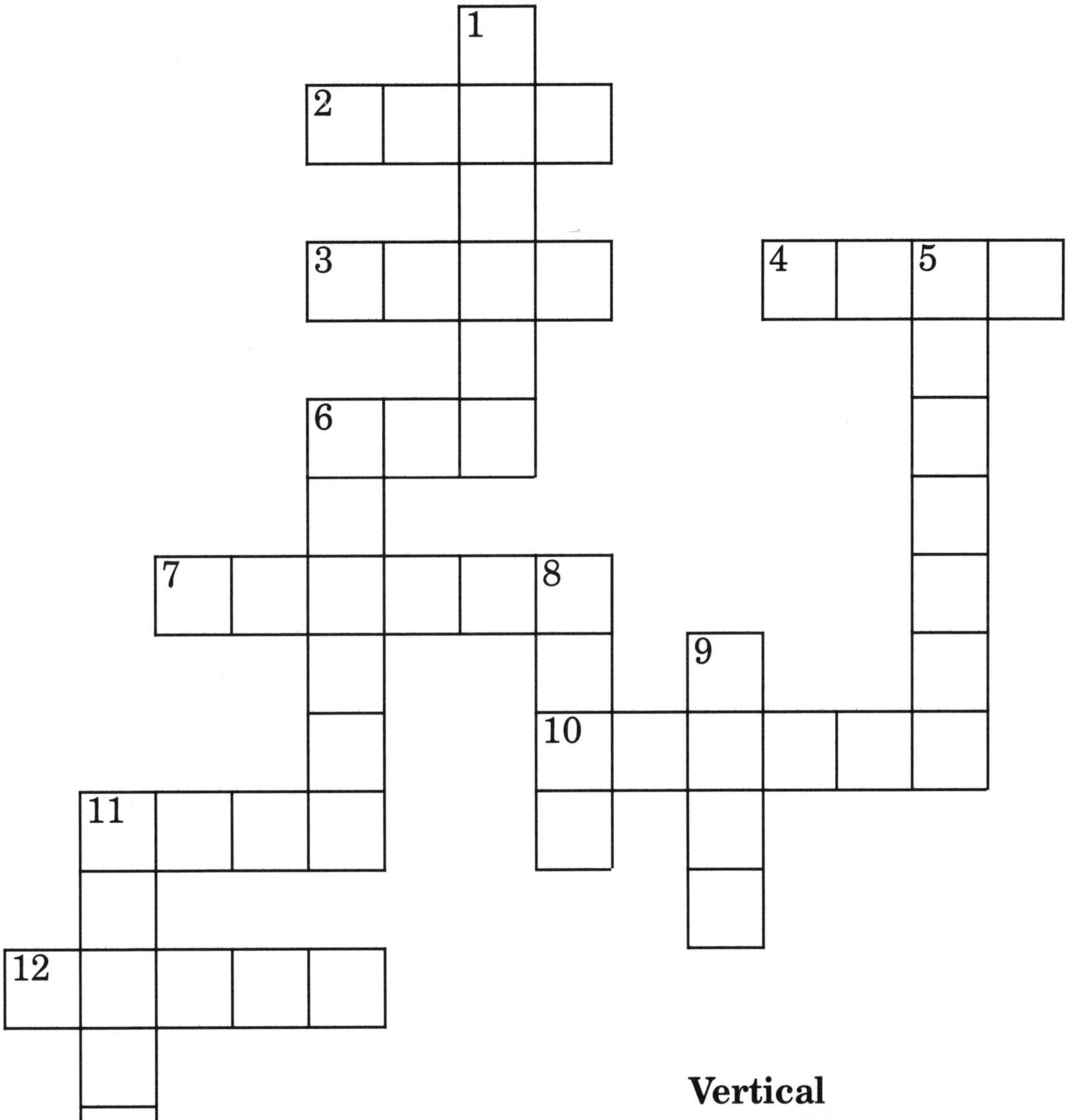

Horizontal

2. 

3. 

4. 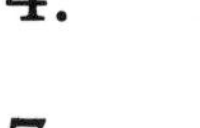

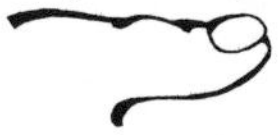

6.

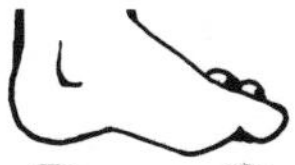

7. 

10.

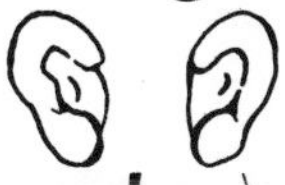

11.

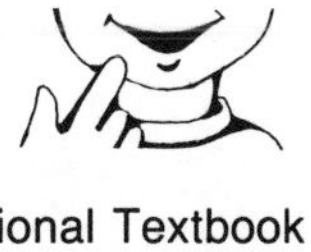

12. 

Vertical

1. 

5. 

6. 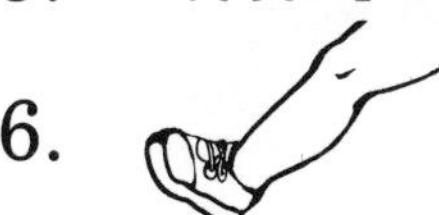

8. 

9. 

11.

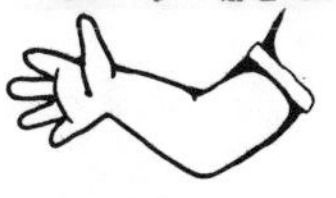

Nombre ____________________

Dibuja y colorea

Lleva una camisa roja.
Lleva pantalones azules.

Lleva una blusa amarilla.
Lleva una falda verde.

¿Sí o no?

1. El niño lleva pantalones verdes. ____________________
2. El niño lleva una blusa roja. ____________________
3. La niña lleva una blusa roja. ____________________
4. La niña lleva un vestido. ____________________
5. La niña lleva una falda verde. ____________________

Nombre ______________________

¿Qué llevas tú?

1. ______________________

2. ______________________

3. ______________________

4. ______________________

5. ______________________

Nombre ______________________________

¿De quién es?

Ropa de niño	Ropa de niña
______________	______________
______________	______________
______________	______________
______________	______________
______________	______________

Ropa de niño o de niña
____
____
____
____
____

calcetines	botas	blusa	pantalones
camisa	falda	suéter	vestido

Nombre ______________________________

¿Qué es?

calcetines • • pantalones

camisa • botas • • blusa

zapatos • • chaqueta

vestido • • suéter gorra • • falda • mitones

Nombre ______________________________

¿Cuál número falta?

doce, trece, ______________________________, quince

once, doce, ______________________________, catorce

dieciséis, diecisiete, ______________________________, diecinueve

catorce, quince, ______________________________, diecisiete

quince, dieciséis, ______________________________, dieciocho

doce, trece, catorce, ______________________________

dieciséis, diecisiete, dieciocho, ______________________________

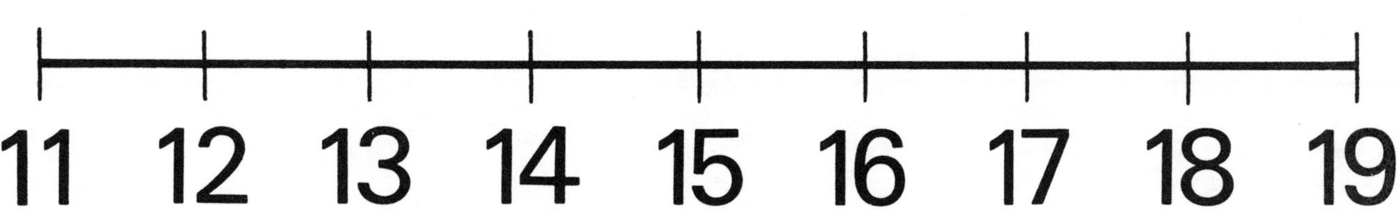

Nombre ______________________________

Corta y pega

mitones	calcetines	botas
chaqueta	suéter	gorra
zapatos	pantalones	vestido

Nombre ______________________________

¿Sí o no?

1. Las señoras llevan guantes. ____________
2. Los zapatos de bebé son grandes. ____________
3. Los niños llevan chaqueta. ____________
4. Los señores llevan abrigo. ____________
5. Los bebés llevan botas de señora. ____________
6. Los señores llevan mitones. ____________
7. Las señoras llevan vestido. ____________
8. Los señores llevan vestido. ____________
9. Los bebés llevan mitones. ____________
10. Los señores llevan botas. ____________

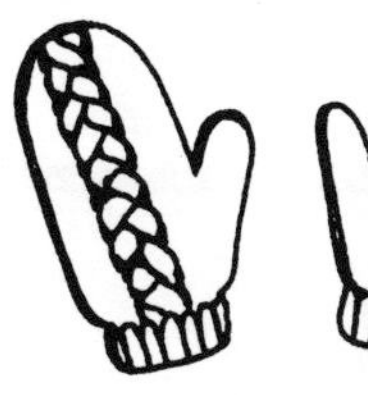

Nombre ____________________

La maestra

Dibuja a la maestra:

¿Qué lleva la maestra? ¿De qué color es la ropa de la maestra?

Nombre ____________________

Fecha ____________________

Contesta

1. ¿Qué día es el treinta?

   ____

2. ¿Qué día es el veintidós?

   ____

3. ¿Qué día es el once?

   ____

4. ¿Qué día es el veinticuatro?

   ____

5. ¿Qué día es el veintiocho?

   ____

6. ¿Qué día es el quince?

   ____

7. ¿Qué día es el doce?

   ____

8. ¿Qué día es el veintinueve?

   ____

Nombre ____________________

Fecha ____________________

Buscapalabras

J K T R E I N T A B X M M B H
M E D I E C I S I E T E V L K
L X O A N X R V Z E Q L W U N
C F E O G W Z A P A T O S S D
Z A V U U D O C E X C E E A O
L X L A W X D I U D A F N B G
Y Q T C T R E C E B T J J J Q
G F B R E B X A E N O X H R V
A A S H R T V Q L I R Q J T V
M L N M U L I O O V C T Y I R
O D Q E C J E N N O E G S O R
M A G C Z C F V E C I Y K V X
I N L X I I X H L S E X I T Q
S F W M R A F V E I N T E Q F
Q R G Q U I N C E H N T X Y B

¿Dónde están las palabras?

once

doce

trece

catorce

quince

diecisiete

veinte

treinta

zapatos

falda

blusa

calcetines

Nombre

Fecha

Nombre ____________________

Fecha ____________________

Crucigrama

Horizontal

1. 

3. 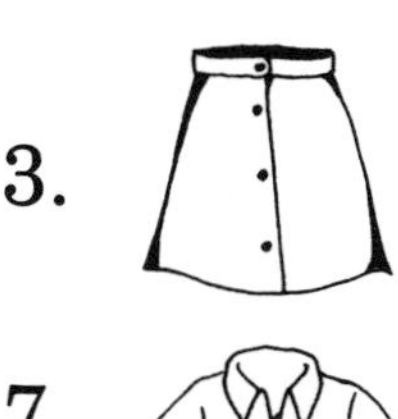

5. 

7.

8. 

Vertical

1. 

2. 

4. 

6.

Nombre ______________________

Fecha ______________________

40

Dibuja

Hace buen tiempo.

¿Qué llevas cuando hace frío?

Hace sol.

Hace calor.

March 5th, 2010

skill, Ph.D.

? 226

pter 4

Nombre ______________________________

Fecha ______________________________

El invierno

hace frío	los guantes	las orejas	la chaqueta
hace calor	el abrigo	junio	tengo calor
enero	los calcetines	tengo frío	febrero

Nombre ______________________

Fecha ______________________

41 Describe

Es un día de ______________.

Hace ______________.

El niño se llama Tony. Tony lleva

______________________ y

______________________. Tony

no tiene ______________.

Contesta

1. ¿Llevas abrigo cuando hace calor? ______________
2. ¿Llevas chaqueta y guantes cuando tienes calor? ______________
3. ¿Hace frío en el invierno? ______________
4. ¿Qué llevas cuando tienes frío? ______________

   ____
5. ¿Qué tiempo hace en mayo? ______________

   ____

Nombre ______________________________

Fecha ______________________________

Completa

Hace frío en ______________________. Cuando tengo frío llevo ______________________, ______________________ y ______________________. No tengo calor en ______________________.

invierno febrero enero botas suéter

chaqueta guantes abrigo mitones

Dibuja

En el invierno

Nombre ______________________________________

Fecha ______________________________________

¿Qué quieren los niños?

Lisa

Marcos

Rosita

Daniel

Maribel

David

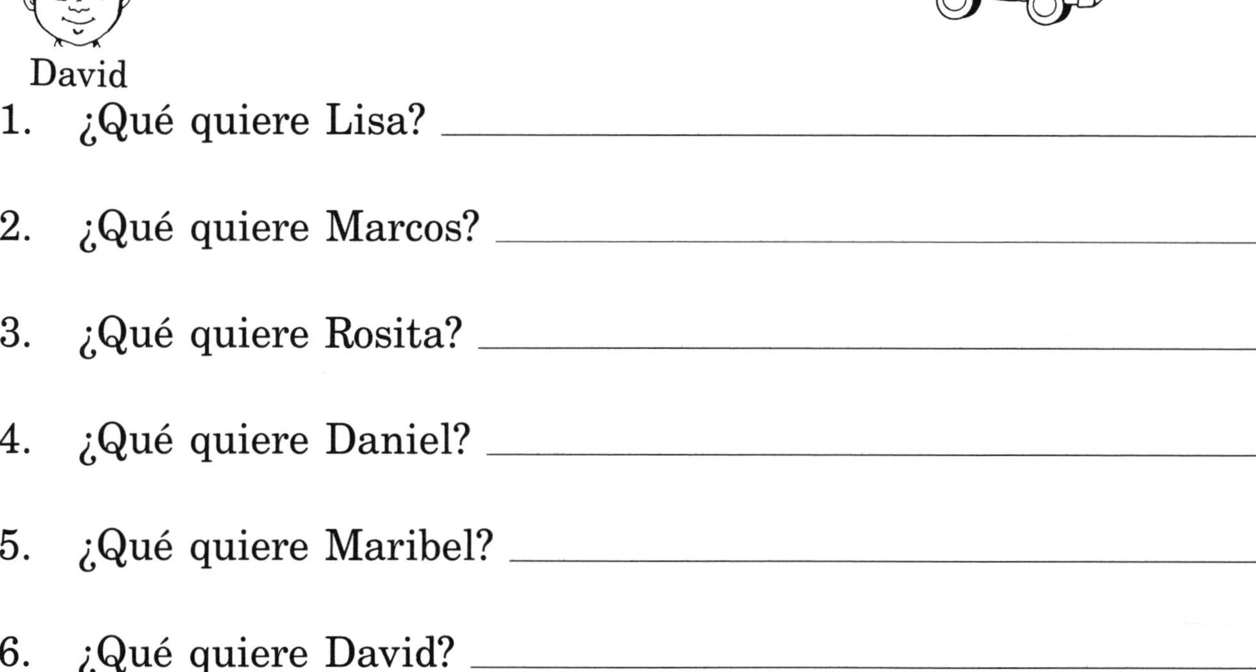

1. ¿Qué quiere Lisa? ______________________________

2. ¿Qué quiere Marcos? ______________________________

3. ¿Qué quiere Rosita? ______________________________

4. ¿Qué quiere Daniel? ______________________________

5. ¿Qué quiere Maribel? ______________________________

6. ¿Qué quiere David? ______________________________

Nombre ____________________

Fecha ____________________

¿Qué tiempo hace?

____

____

____

____

____

____

____

____

____

Nombre ______________________________

Fecha ______________________________

Los juguetes

1. Colorea la cometa verde.

2. Dibuja una niña con el pito.

3. Dibuja un niño con la pelota.

4. Dibuja un bebé con la muñeca.

5. Escribe el número seis en la puerta del coche.

6. Escribe una X en un juguete que no tienes.

7. Escribe tu nombre en un juguete que quieres tener.

Nombre ______________________

Fecha ______________________

¿Qué quieres tú?

Los juguetes que tengo	Los juguetes que quiero tener
______	______
______	______
______	______
______	______
______	______
______	______
______	______
______	______
______	______
______	______

Nombre ______________________________

Fecha ______________________________

Crucigrama

Horizontal

2. 

3. 

4. 

5. 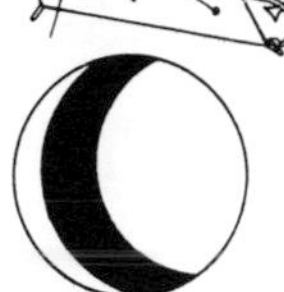

7. 

8. 

Vertical

1. 

3. 

6.

7.

Nombre ______________________________

Fecha ______________________________

En mi escuela

El principal (La principal) se llama

______________________________.

El conserje se llama

______________________________.

La secretaria se llama

______________________________.

La enfermera se llama

______________________________.

La bibliotecaria (el bibliotecario) se llama

______________________________.

Estoy en ______________________________ grado.

Nombre ______________________________

Fecha ______________________________

¿Adónde va Luis?

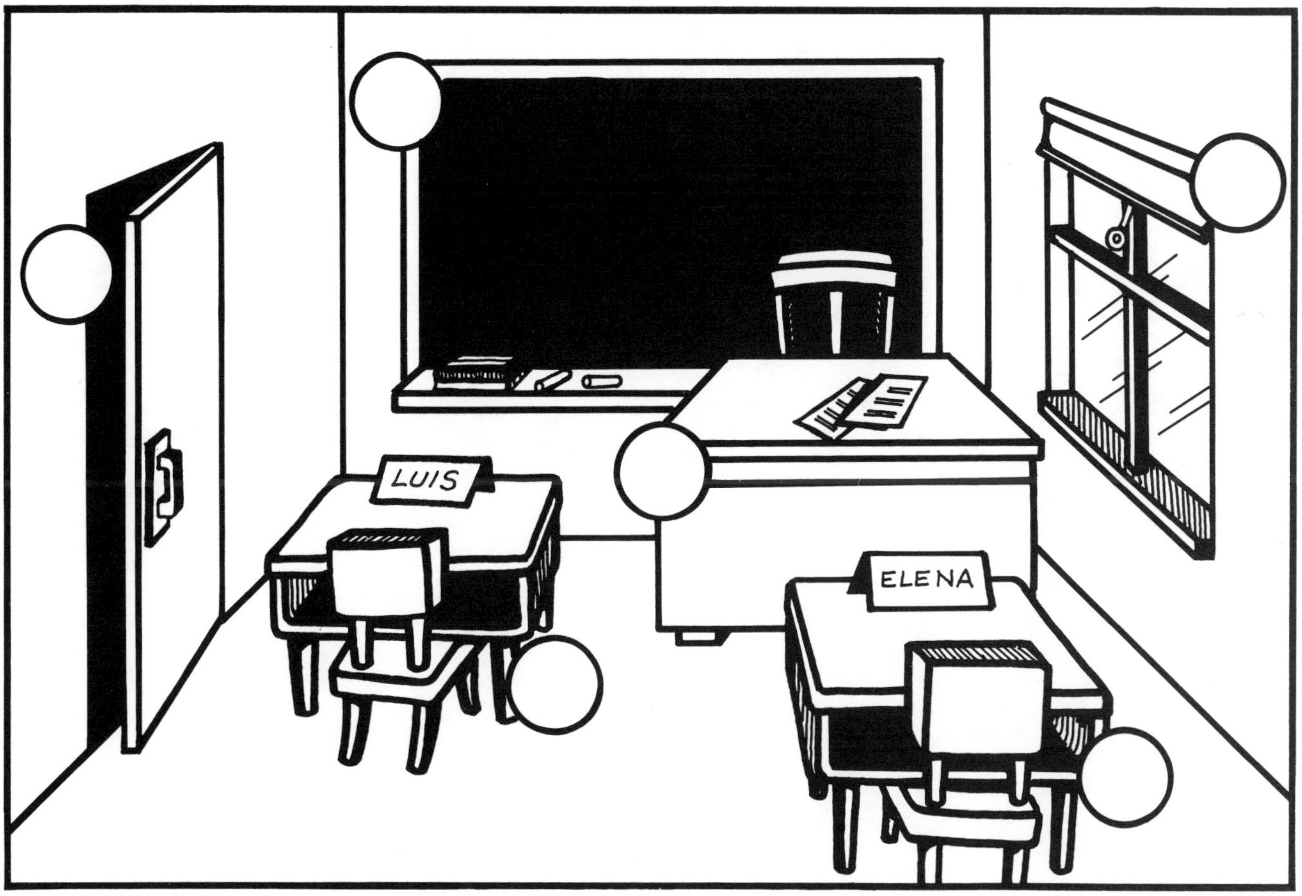

La maestra: Luis, ¿Adónde vas?

Luis: Señorita, . . .

1. voy a la puerta.
2. voy al pupitre de Elena.
3. voy a la pizarra.
4. voy al pupitre de la maestra.
5. voy a la ventana.
6. voy a mi pupitre.

Nombre ____________________

Fecha ____________________

¿Adónde vas?

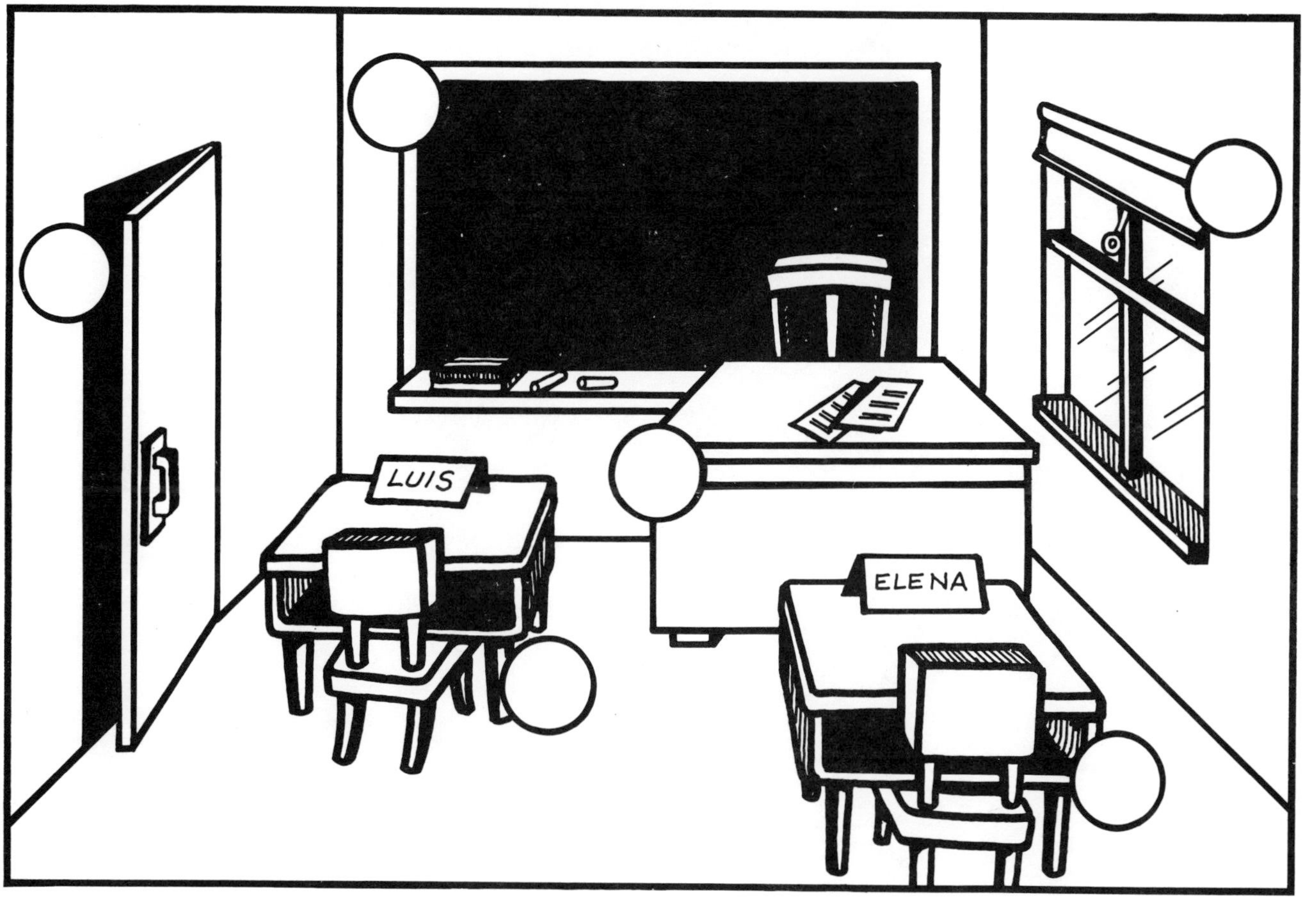

1. Voy a ____________________

2. ____________________

3. ____________________

4. ____________________

5. ____________________

Nombre ____________________

Fecha ____________________

¿Adónde van?

¡Vayan a la silla de la maestra!

¡Vayan a la pizarra!

¡Vayan al pupitre de un niño!

¡Vayan al pupitre de una niña que lleva pantalones!

¡Vayan a la puerta!

¡Vayan a una ventana!

¡Vayan a la bandera!

¡Vayan a la silla de un niño con pelo negro!

Nombre ______________________

Fecha ______________________

El juego de va con

El papel va con ______________________

El pelo ______________________

El brazo ______________________

La falda ______________________

La secretaria ______________________

La silla ______________________

La cometa ______________________

Los calcetines van con ______________________

Los dientes ______________________

Los pantalones ______________________

la blusa

el lápiz

los zapatos

la camisa

la cabeza

la mano

la oficina

la boca

el pupitre

el viento

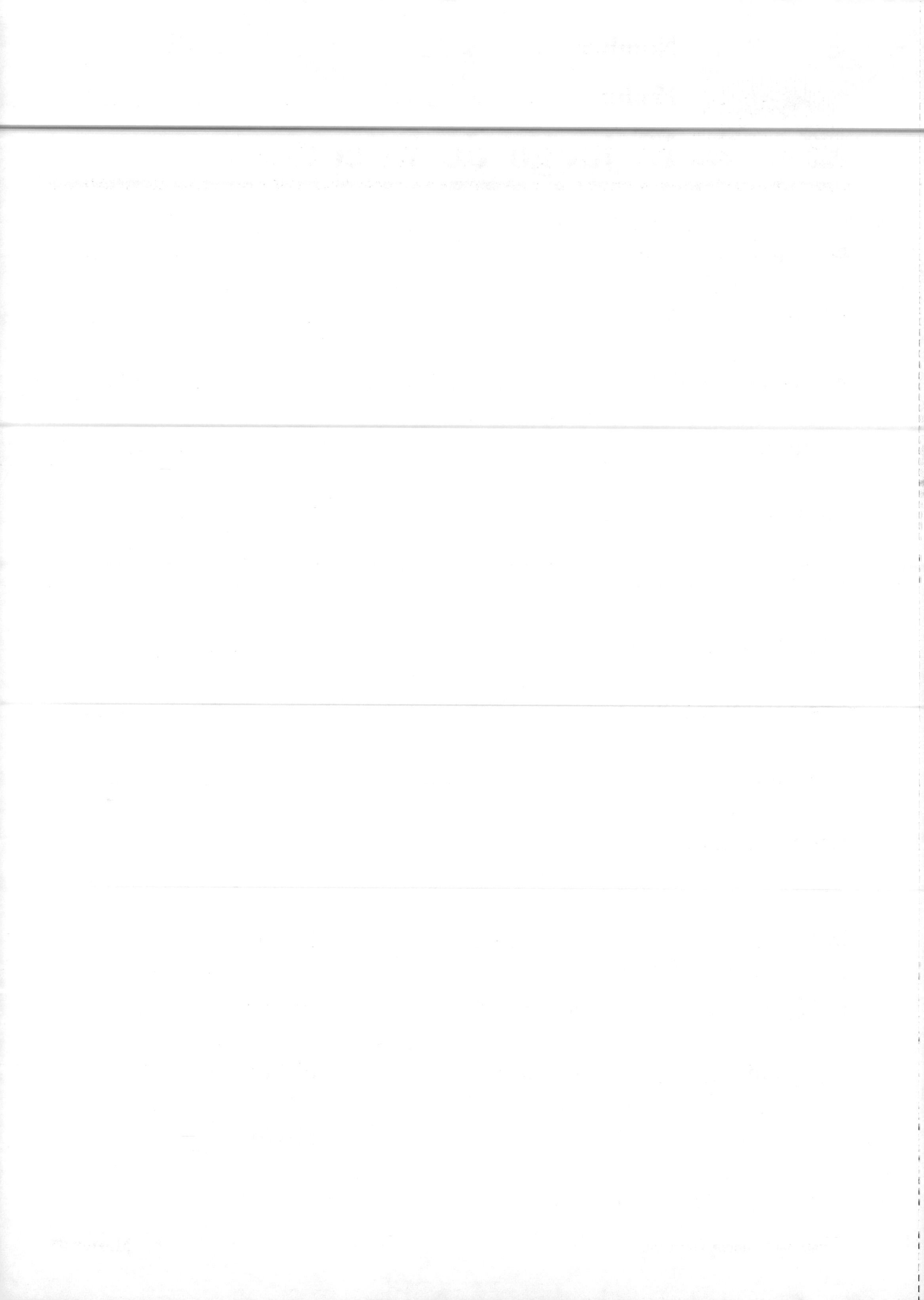

Nombre ______________________________

Fecha ______________________________

¿Qué hacen los niños?

____

____

____

____

____

____

Nombre ______________________

Fecha ______________________

Lee y contesta

Cuando hace buen tiempo, los niños juegan en el patio de recreo.
Hay un patio de recreo en la escuela.
Los niños juegan en el patio de recreo.
Corren y brincan la cuerda en el patio de recreo.
No juegan en la clase. Juegan en el patio de recreo.
No corren en la clase. Corren en el patio de recreo.
No juegan en la oficina. Juegan en el patio de recreo.
No brincan la cuerda en la oficina.
Brincan la cuerda en el patio de recreo.

1. ¿Quiénes juegan en el patio de recreo? ______________________

   ____

2. ¿Qué hacen los niños en el patio de recreo? ______________________

   ______________________ y ______________________

3. ¿Tiene tu escuela un patio de recreo? ______________________

   ____

4. ¿Brincas la cuerda en el patio de recreo? ______________________

   ____

5. ¿Juegas a la pelota en el patio de recreo? ______________________

   ____

Nombre ______________________________

Fecha ______________________________

La clase está en fila

1.

2.

3.

4.

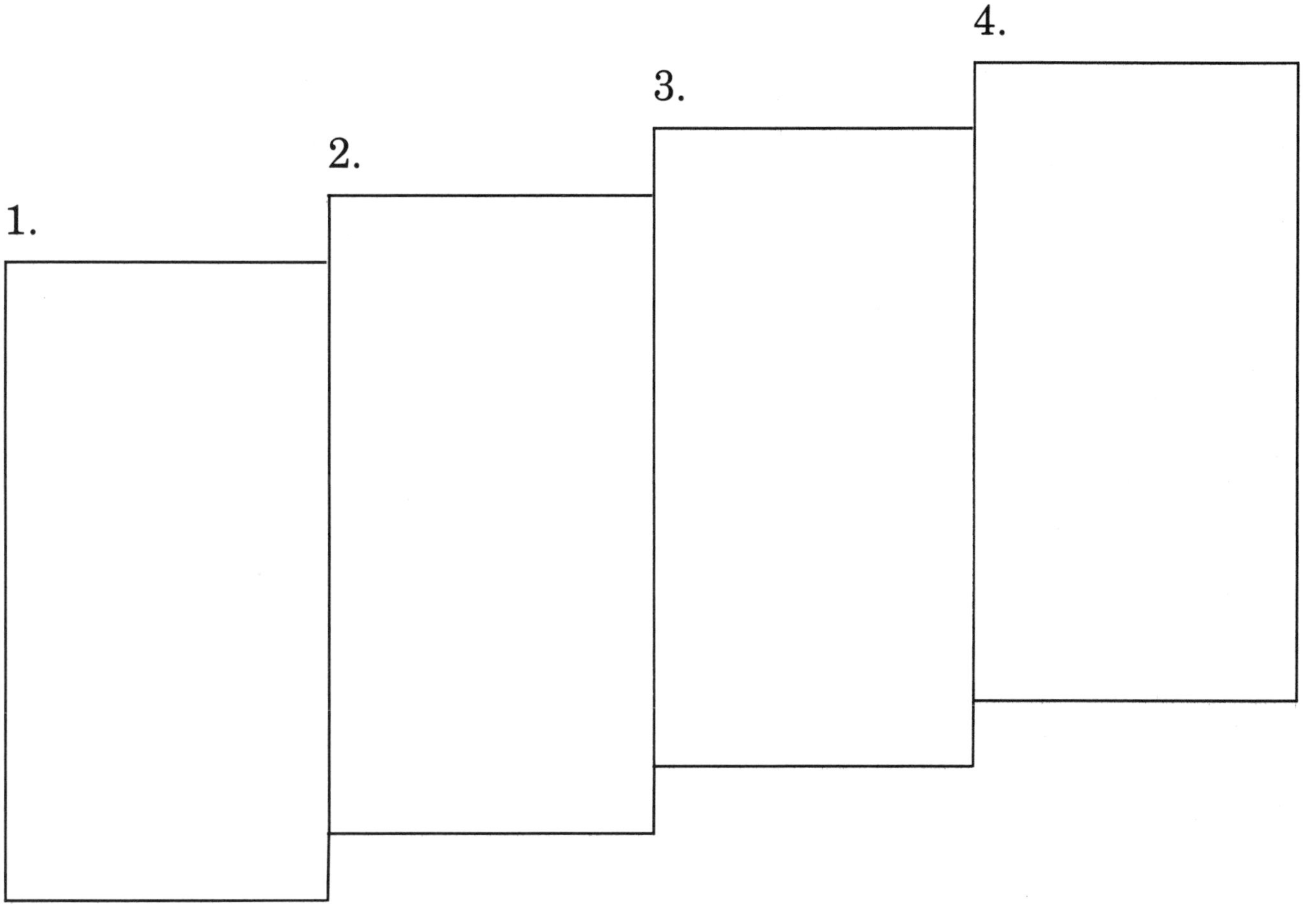

A. Enrique es primero.
B. Toni es segunda.
C. Linda es tercera.
D. Paco está detrás de Linda.

Nombre ____________________

Fecha ____________________

En el patio de recreo

1. ¿Dónde están los niños? ____________________

____

2. ¿Qué hacen?

a. Una niña ____________________.

b. Una niña ____________________.

c. El niño ____________________.

Nombre ________________________________

Fecha ________________________________

Frases secretas

1. la oficina. La principal en trabaja

____

2. la biblioteca. libros mucho Hay en

____

3. al patio de recreo Los niños para jugar. van

____

4. afuera. está El patio de recreo

____

5. la clase. en No corro

____

6. brincan la cuerda. Los niños

____

Nombre ______________________________

Fecha ______________________________

¿Qué le falta?

1. **La maestra:** Tato, ¡escribe en la pizarra!

Tato: Señorita, ¡no tengo tiza! ¿Dónde está la tiza?

¡Quiero la tiza! Quiero escribir con la tiza.

La maestra: Tato quiere escribir en la pizarra.

Quiere escribir, pero no tiene tiza para escribir.

¿Qué le falta?

Tú: Le falta ______________________________.

2. **La maestra:** Tato, ¡escribe en el papel con un lápiz!

Tato: Señorita, quiero escribir pero no tengo lápiz.

¡No tengo lápiz!

La maestra: ¿Qué te falta Tato?

Tato: Me ______________________________.

3. **La maestra:** Tato, ¡juega en el patio de recreo con la cuerda!

Tato: Sí, sí, señorita.

Quiero jugar en el patio de recreo con la cuerda.

Quiero jugar pero no tengo una cuerda.

La maestra: Sí Tato, no tienes una cuerda.

______________ falta una cuerda.

Nombre ______________________

Fecha ______________________

El cumpleaños

El mes	Nombre
enero	
febrero	
marzo	
abril	
mayo	
junio	
julio	
agosto	
septiembre	
octubre	
noviembre	
diciembre	

Nombre ____________________

Fecha ____________________

Los meses

Treinta días tiene septiembre,
abril, junio y noviembre;
febrero tiene veintiocho,
y los demás treinta y uno.

Escribe

Treinta días tiene ____________________,

____________________, junio y ____________________;

____________________ tiene veintiocho,

y los demás ____________________.

Contesta

¿Cuántos días hay en septiembre? ____________________

¿Cuántos días hay en abril? ____________________

¿Cuántos días hay en junio? ____________________

¿Cuántos días hay en noviembre? ____________________

¿Cuántos días hay en febrero? ____________________

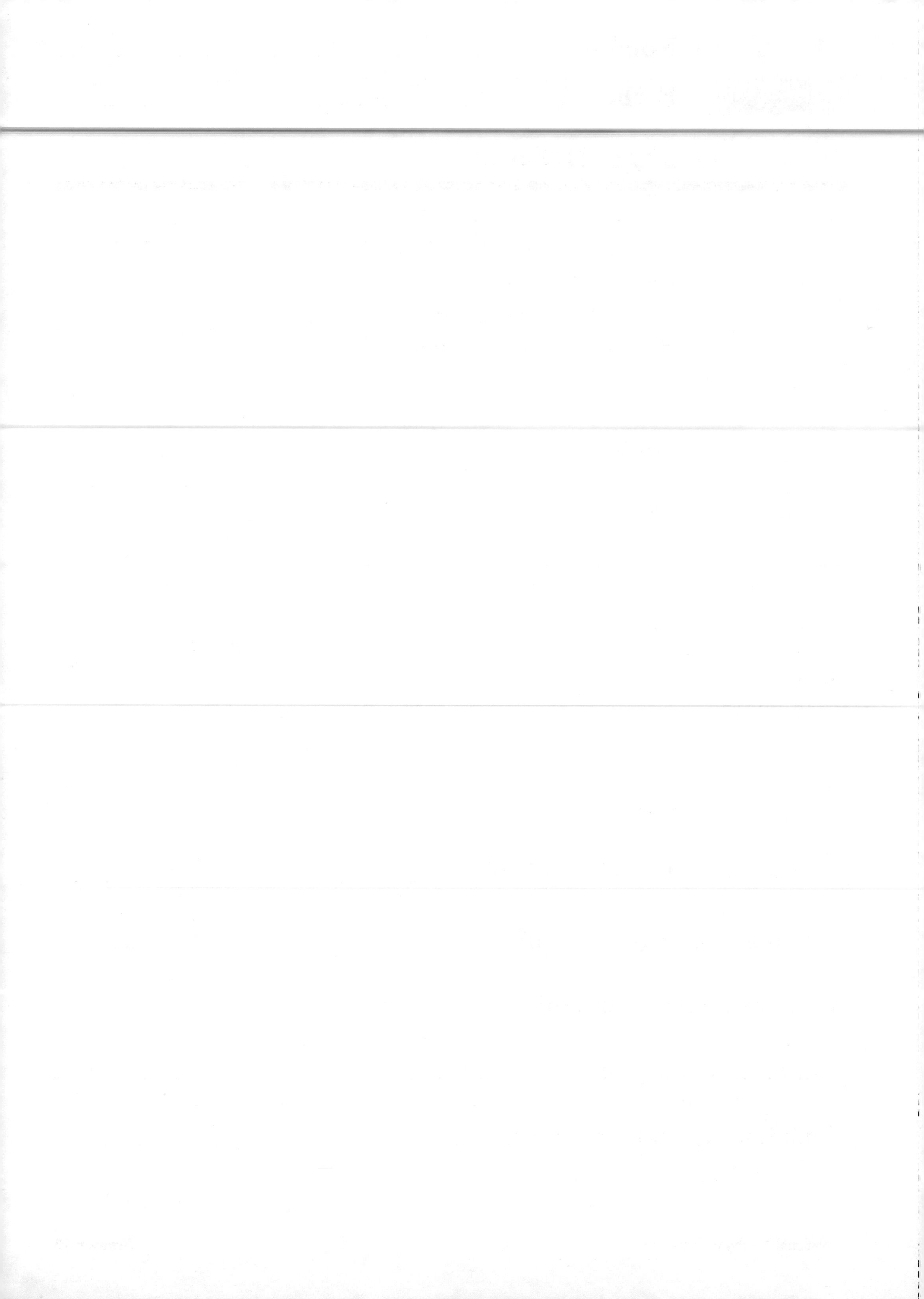

Nombre ______________________

Fecha ______________________

¿Qué va a hacer Tato?

1. ______________________

____

2. ______________________

____

3. ______________________

____

4. ______________________

____

5. ______________________

____

6. ______________________

____

Nombre ______________________________

Fecha ______________________________

En la clase de español

1.	Hablo español.	Sí	No
2.	Hablo inglés.	Sí	No
3.	Hablo cuando habla la maestra.	Sí	No
4.	Hablo cuando habla un niño.	Sí	No
5.	Hablo cuando el principal (o la principal) está en mi clase.	Sí	No
6.	Hablo por teléfono.	Sí	No
7.	Hablo con una muñeca.	Sí	No
8.	La maestra habla español.	Sí	No
9.	La maestra habla inglés.	Sí	No
10.	La maestra habla con los niños.	Sí	No
11.	La maestra habla por teléfono.	Sí	No
12.	La maestra habla con una muñeca.	Sí	No

Nombre ______________________

Fecha ______________________

Escribo en español

1. ¿Qué día es hoy? ¿Cuál es la fecha?

____

____

2. ¿Cuándo es tu cumpleaños?

____

3. ¿Qué hablas en la clase de español?

____

4. ¿Hablas por teléfono? ¿Con quién?

____

5. Cuando hace viento y quieres jugar afuera, ¿qué te falta?

____

Dibuja

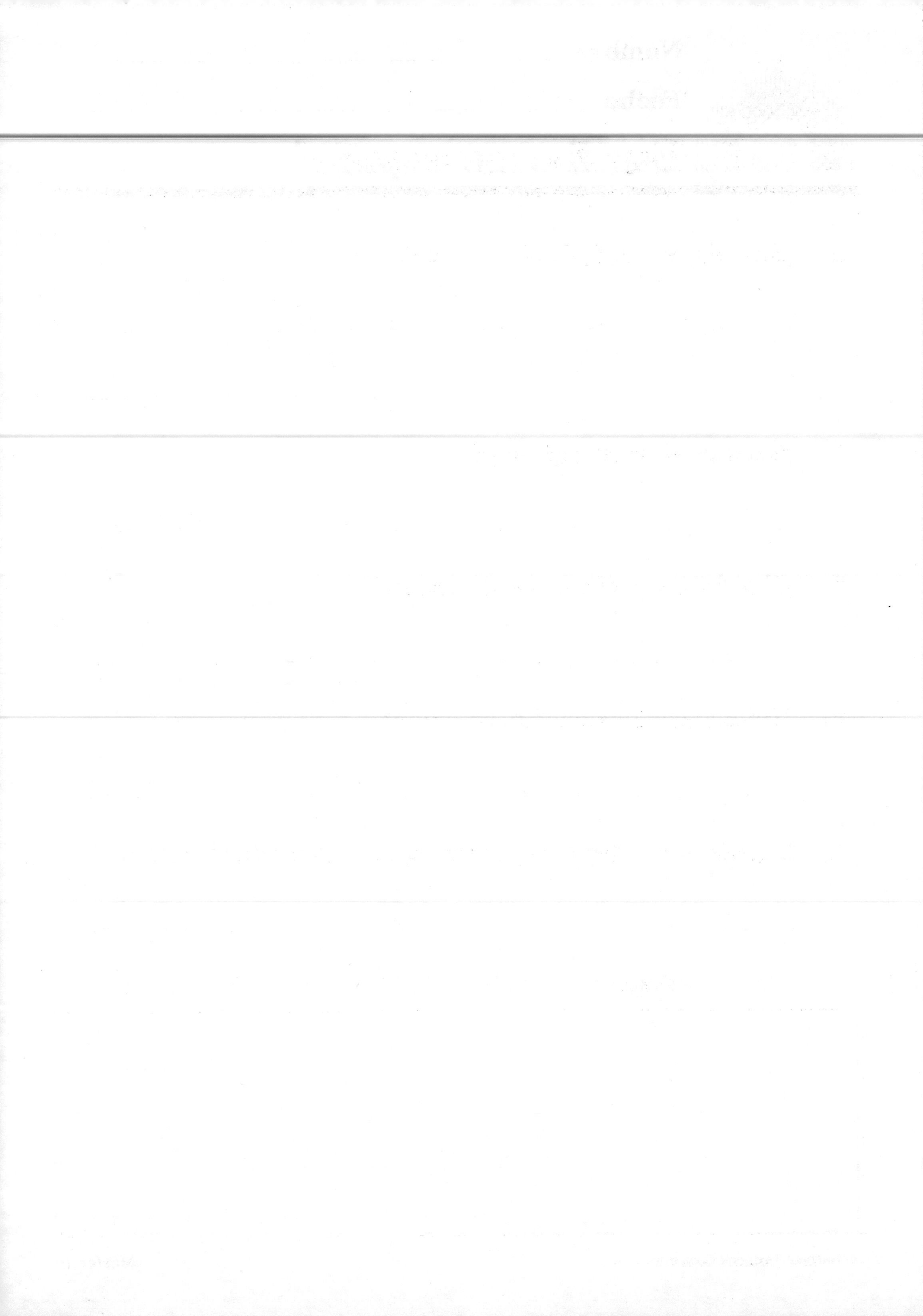

Nombre ____________________

Fecha ____________________

En la clase

Dos niños están en la clase:

Manuel: ¿Quieres jugar afuera?

Susana: Sí. Quiero jugar afuera.

¿Qué vamos a jugar?

Manuel: Quiero jugar a la rayuela, ¿y tú?

Susana: Yo quiero brincar la cuerda, pero me falta una cuerda.

Manuel: ¿Quieres jugar a la pelota?

Susana: Sí, quiero. ¿Tienes una pelota?

Manuel: No. No tengo una pelota.

Quiero jugar a la pelota pero me falta una pelota.

Susana: Tengo mis patines. ¿Tienes tus patines?

Manuel: Sí, tengo mis patines.

¡Vamos afuera a jugar!

Dibuja

¿Con qué van a jugar Manuel y Susana?

Nombre ____________________

Fecha ____________________

El teléfono

Pepe no está en la escuela.

Quiere hablar con Juana. Habla por ____________________.

No habla inglés. Habla ____________________.

Pepe: ¡Hola Juana!

Juana: ¿Quién habla?

Pepe: ____________________ Pepe.

Juana: ¡Hola, ____________________! ¿Qué tal?

Pepe: ____________________, gracias.

¿Quieres ____________________ con mi juguete?

Juana: ¿Qué es?

¿Es grande o es ____________________?

Pepe: No es grande. No es pequeño.

El juguete es para jugar afuera cuando hace viento.

Voy a jugar afuera.

Quiero jugar afuera porque hace viento.

¿Qué es mi juguete?

Juana: ¡Tu juguete es una ____________________!

Nombre ______________________________

Fecha ______________________________

La familia de Marta

1. ______________________________ habla por teléfono.

2. ______________________________ juega con el bebé.

3. ______________________________ del bebé brinca la cuerda.

4. ______________________________ grande del bebé juega con el camión.

5. ______________________________ pequeño dibuja en un libro con un creyón.

6. La familia del bebé tiene ______________________________, un ______________________________, una ______________________________ y dos ______________________________.

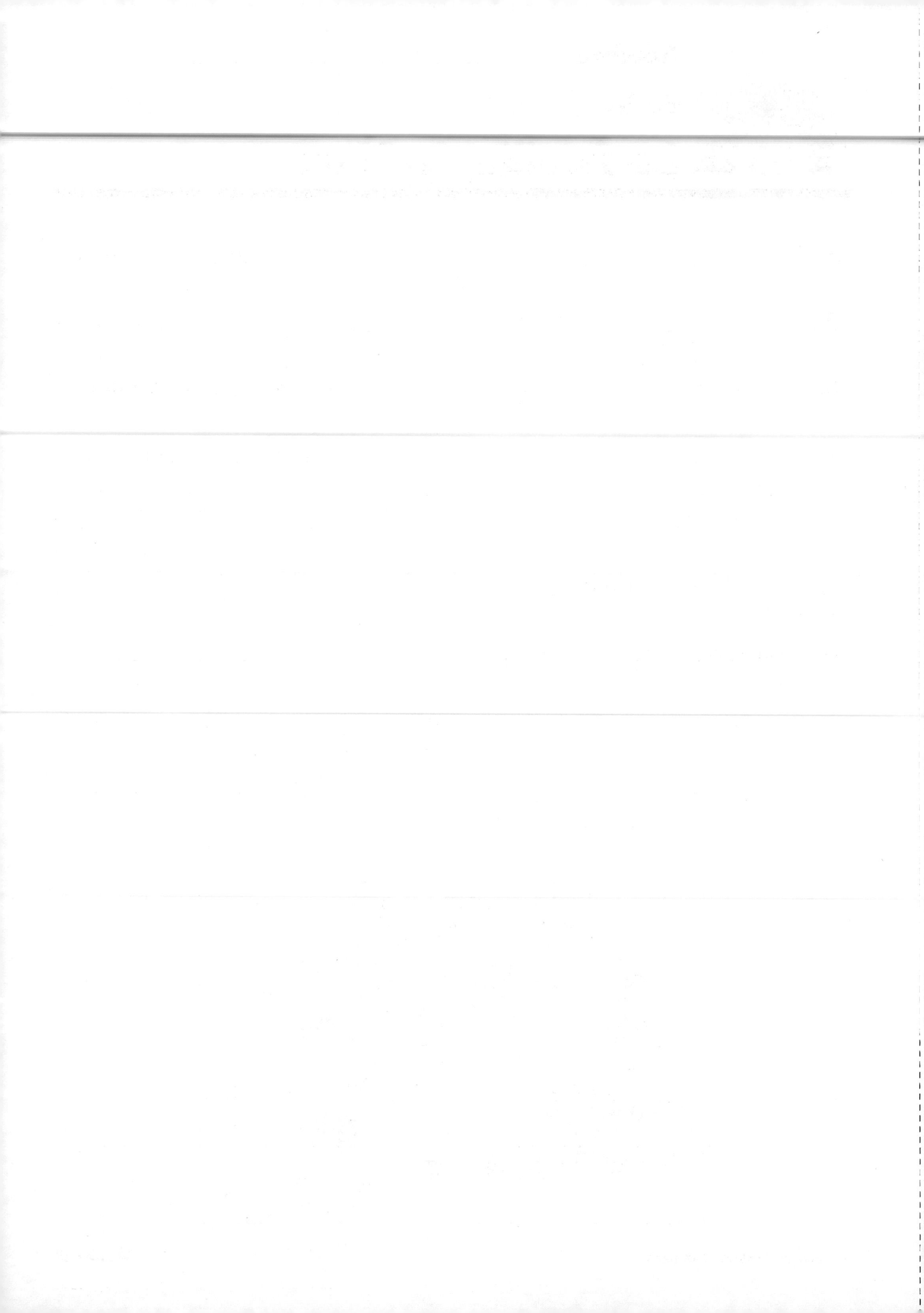

Nombre ______________________________

Fecha ______________________________

¿Quién soy yo?

Me llamo ______________________________.

Vivo en ______________________________.

Mi número de teléfono es ______________________________.

Tengo ______________________________ abuelos.

Mis abuelos viven en ______________________________.

Mis abuelos se llaman ______________________________,

______________________________, ______________________________.

Mis abuelos

Nombre ______________________________

Fecha ______________________________

Aparea

la casa

el abuelo

el papá

los hijos

los padres

la mamá

el perro

el bebé

la abuela

el gato

los abuelos

el apartamento

Nombre ____________________

Fecha ____________________

¿Dónde viven?

1. Hay cuatro personas en la familia.
   Hay dos hijas.
   Tienen un gato.
   ¿En qué apartamento viven?

   ____

2. Hay tres personas en la familia.
   Hay un hijo.
   La familia no tiene un gato.
   La familia no tiene un perro.
   ¿En qué apartamento viven?

   ____

3. Hay cuatro personas en la familia.
   Los abuelos viven con la familia.
   No tienen un gato.
   No tienen un perro.
   ¿En qué apartamento viven?

   ____

4. Hay tres personas en la familia.
   La familia tiene un hijo.
   La familia tiene un perro.
   ¿En qué apartamento viven?

   ____

Nombre ______________________________

Fecha ______________________________

Contesta

1. ¿Dónde vive tu familia, en una casa o en un apartamento?

____

2. ¿Viven tus abuelos con tu familia?

____

3. ¿Viven tus abuelos en una casa o en un apartamento?

____

4. ¿Cuántos hijos tiene tu mamá?

____

5. ¿Cuántas hijas tiene tu mamá?

____

6. ¿Cuántos hijos tiene tu abuela?

____

7. ¿Cuántas hijas tiene tu abuela?

____

8. ¿Tienes un gato?

____

9. ¿Tienes un perro?

____

10. ¿Tienes un bebé en tu familia?

____

Nombre ______________________

Fecha ______________________

¿Quién es?

En tu casa, ¿quién . . .

1. habla mucho por teléfono? ______________________
2. tiene su cumpleaños en el invierno? ______________________
3. tiene una bicicleta? ______________________
4. habla inglés? ______________________
5. habla español? ______________________
6. tiene un coche? ______________________
7. tiene una muñeca? ______________________
8. no lleva mitones cuando hace frío? ______________________
9. no juega con tus juguetes? ______________________
10. lleva pantalones? ______________________

Nombre ______________________________

Fecha ______________________________

¡Tengo tíos y primos!

Dibuja a tu tío,
a tu tía o a
tus tíos.

¿Cómo se llama(n)?

____

¿Tiene(n) hijos?
Dibuja: a tu primo,
a tu prima o a tus
primos.

¿Cómo se llama(n)?

____

Contesta

1. ¿Tienes un tío? ______________________

   ¿Cómo se llama? ______________________

   ¿Tienes una tía? ______________________

   ¿Cómo se llama? ______________________

2. ¿Cuántos primos tienes? ______________________

Nombre ______________________________

Fecha ______________________________

Las personas de nuestra clase

¿Cuántas personas . . .	Número
1. viven en un apartamento?	________
2. tienen tres personas en su familia?	________
3. tienen un hermano?	________
4. tienen dos hermanas?	________
5. tienen un bebé?	________
6. tienen un gato?	________
7. tienen un perro?	________
8. viven con sus abuelos?	________
9. tienen muchos tíos?	________
10. no tienen muchos primos?	________
11. tienen un primo en esta escuela?	________
12. tienen una prima en esta escuela?	________

Nombre ____________________

Fecha ____________________

Mi amigo

Su nombre: ____________________

Hay ____________________ personas en su familia.

Tiene ____________________ hermanos.

Tiene ____________________ hermanas.

	Sí	No
Tiene un gato.	☐	☐
Tiene un perro.	☐	☐
Tiene una bicicleta.	☐	☐
Tiene una muñeca.	☐	☐
Vive en una casa.	☐	☐
Vive en un apartamento.	☐	☐

Nombre ______________________________

Fecha ______________________________

¿Dónde viven?

un señor	un perro	un gato	una abuela
un gallo	una vaca	un bebé	
una niña	un caballo	una gallina	

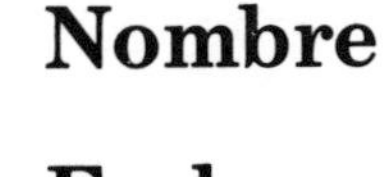

Nombre ______________________________

Fecha ______________________________

¡Qué animales!

Dibuja

Al conejo le falta una pata.

Una oveja con alas.

Un pato con un pescuezo muy grande.

Un cordero con una cola pequeña y con orejas grandes.

Nombre ______________________

Fecha ______________________

Crucigrama

Horizontal

2. 

5. 

6. 

8. 

9. 

10. 

Vertical

1. 

3. 

4. 

7. 

Nombre ______________________

Fecha ______________________

Las familias de los animales

el animal	la mamá	el papá	el bebé

Contesta

1. El papá del pollito es el ______________________.
2. La mamá del becerro es la ______________________.
3. El bebé de la pata es el ______________________.

el gallo	el becerro	el pato
la vaca	la pata	la gallina
el patito	el pollito	el toro

Nombre ______________________

Fecha ______________________

Un animal imaginario

Dibuja

63 Un animal imaginario *(página 2)*

Contesta

1. ¿Dónde vive tu animal imaginario, en el establo, en la casa o afuera? ______________________
2. ¿Es grande o pequeño? ______________________
3. ¿Tiene alas? ¿Cuántas? ______________________

____
4. ¿Tiene un pescuezo grande o pequeño? ______________________

____
5. ¿Tiene patas? ¿Cuántas? ______________________

____
6. ¿Tiene cola? ¿Cuántas? ______________________

____
7. ¿Qué dice? ______________________

____
8. ¿Cómo se llama? ______________________

Nombre ______________________

Fecha ______________________

¿Cuál palabra va bien?

1. cuatro seis. . .	cinco sí ocho
2. gallo gallina. . .	pollito patito becerro
3. muñeca patines. . .	cometa suéter tiza
4. botas guantes. . .	rayuela abrigo rojo
5. invierno frío. . .	calor nieva julio
6. lunes viernes. . .	domingo veintidós el conserje
7. ojo nariz. . .	boca abril lápiz
8. la principal la maestra. . .	el teléfono el pavo la bibliotecaria
9. rojo amarillo. . .	grande mucho verde
10. once doce. . .	trece camión tres

Nombre ____________________

Fecha ____________________

¿Qué es? ¿De qué color es?

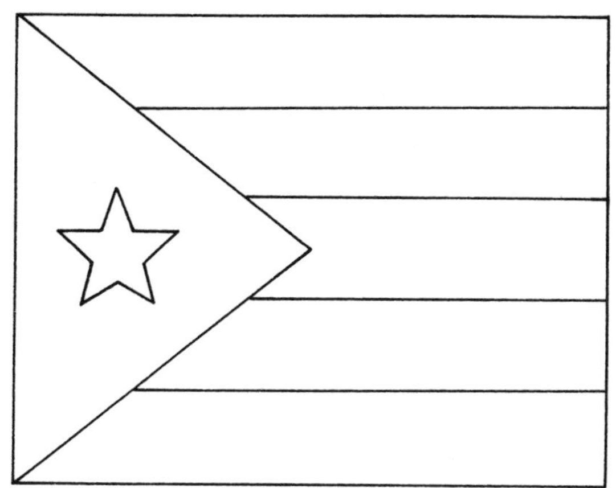

____________________ ____________________

____

____________________ ____________________

Nombre ______________________

Fecha ______________________

¿Sí o no?

	Las personas	Los animales
1. Tienen patas.	________	________
2. Llevan pantalones.	________	________
3. Tienen boca.	________	________
4. Tienen alas.	________	________
5. Juegan con juguetes.	________	________
6. Tienen ojos.	________	________
7. Hablan español.	________	________
8. Tienen cola.	________	________
9. Viven en la oficina.	________	________
10. Tienen familias.	________	________

Nombre ______________________________

Fecha ______________________________

¿Para qué es...?

1. ¿Para qué es la boca? ______________________________

2. ¿Para qué es la tiza? ______________________________

3. ¿Para qué es una cometa? ______________________________

4. ¿Para qué son los pies? ______________________________

5. ¿Para qué son los calcetines? ______________________________

6. ¿Para qué es el teléfono? ______________________________

7. ¿Para qué es la pasta? ______________________________

8. ¿Para qué es la cuerda? ______________________________

9. ¿Para qué son los creyones? ______________________________

10. ¿Para qué son las tijeras? ______________________________

Nombre ______________________________

Fecha ______________________________

Crucigrama

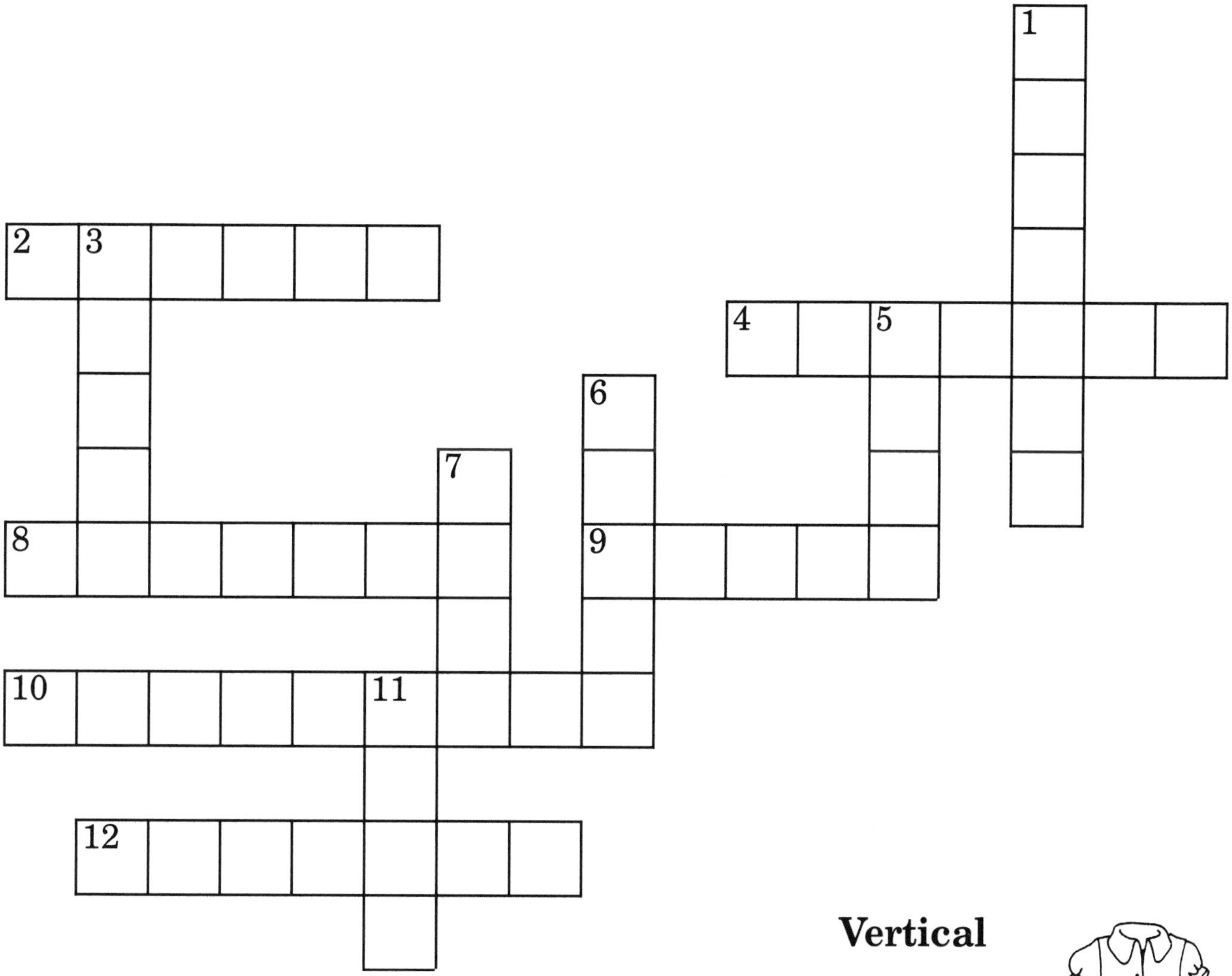

Horizontal

2. 
4. 
8. 
9. 
10. 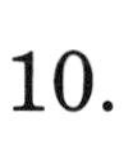
12. 

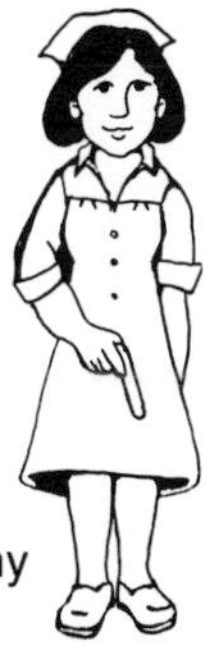

Vertical

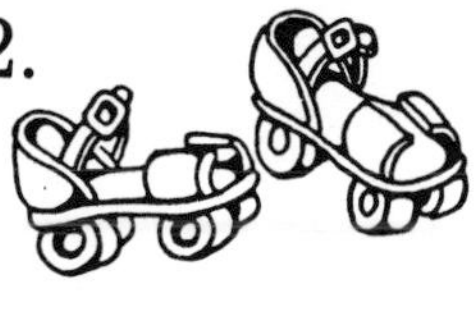

1. 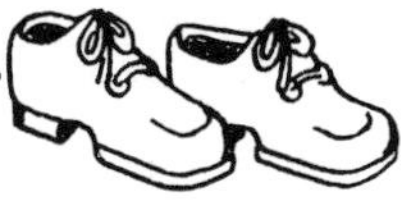 
3. 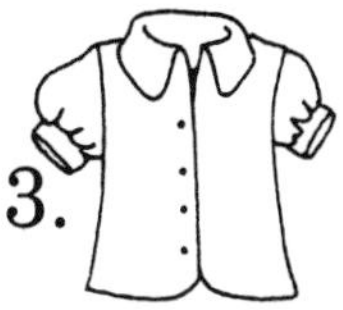 
5.
6.
7. **12**
11.